I CAN'T FIND A HEARTBEAT

I CAN'T FIND A HEARTBEAT

*Hope and Help for Those
Who Have Lost an Unborn Child*

MELISSA SEXSON HANSON

REVIEW AND HERALD® PUBLISHING ASSOCIATION
HAGERSTOWN, MD 21740

The author assumes full responsibility for the accuracy of all facts and quotations as cited in this book. The opinions expressed are those of the author and not necessarily those of the editor, publisher, or the Seventh-day Adventist Church.

This book was
Edited by Jeannette R. Johnson
Copyedited by Jocelyn Fay and James Cavil
Designed by Willie S. Duke
Electronic make-up by Shirley M. Bolivar
Cover photo by Tony Stone Images
Typeset: 11/14 Stempel Schneidler

PRINTED IN U.S.A.

03 02 01 00 99   5 4 3 2 1

R&H Cataloging Service
Hanson, Melissa Sexson, 1967-

    I can't find a heartbeat: hope and help
for those who have lost an unborn child.

      1. Miscarriage I. Title

          618.392

ISBN 0-8280-1347-0

This book is lovingly dedicated to my first child,

whom I lost at the end of my first trimester. May the miracle of

your short life be a heartbeat of inspiration to those who are search-

ing for God's hope and healing.

Special thanks for those
who helped make the dream
of this book a reality . . .

Ken Hanson,
for his unending encouragement as a
supportive husband.

Denny and Janice Sexson,
for their helpful suggestions and loving assistance.

Doug and Wilma Bing,
Randy and Ruth Davis,
and Selma Mohr,
for their thoughtful recommendations in the
proofreading and editing of this book.

Wilma Bing,
Aaron and Evelyn Moon,
Susan Peters,
Melody Rockufeler,
Greg Rumsey, and
Elwood and Amy Sherrard,
for sharing their wisdom and advice in the
construction of a query letter.

CONTENTS

In December 1997 Ann Marie H. Bates and her husband lost their son in the fifth month of her pregnancy: "The child lost is no less a part of our hearts and our lives because he was with us for such a short time. We have asked the Lord to turn our loss into comfort for others. Perhaps this poem is one way He can do that."

Zachary
From the very beginning, you have been a part of me;
a beautiful gift of life and love
from the imagination of the Creator.
I dreamed of you.
Would your eyes be blue or green or brown¿
Would you be quiet and thoughtful,
or full of exuberant curiosity¿
I never had the chance to discover you.
Darkness stole you away,
though I wanted desperately to hold on to you.
Sleep now, little one, if you must;
the darkness is not too deep for Him who is coming
to open your eyes,
to restore your life in perfection.
On that day I will look for you,
and heaven will deliver you to my empty arms.
Then I will watch you grow,
unfolding your beauty in the eternal light of our Redeemer.
—Ann Marie Bates

Chapter 1

GREAT EXPECTATIONS

*Trust in the Lord, and do good. . . . Delight yourself also in the Lord,
and He shall give you the desires of your heart. Commit your way to the
Lord, trust also in Him, and He shall bring it to pass. . . . Rest in the
Lord, and wait patiently for Him. Ps. 37:3-7, NKJV.*

Glancing around the sterile examination room,
I felt my heart quicken. I'd been in this room
many times in the past, but never had the
excitement surged through me as it did at this
moment. Always before I had come with a great longing
in my heart, a burning desire that haunted me day
and night.

But today would be different. Today joy grew inside
me, filling my deepest need. A slow grin spread across
Ken's face as his eyes met mine. I wasn't the only one
who'd been waiting for this moment. Twelve weeks had
passed—12 weeks of planning and praising God for this
precious gift. Now, at last, we would hear our baby's
heartbeat for the first time.

My thoughts flashed back to the surgery I'd had at 16
for a bilateral teratoma tumor, a very rare birth defect that
usually doesn't appear in a woman until she's past childbearing age. The tumor, as big as a grapefruit, had com-

pletely engulfed one of my ovaries and partially covered the other. The doctor had been forced to remove all but one fourth of one ovary, as well as one of my fallopian tubes. As a child I had loved playing house with my dolls, pretending to be their mother. As a teen I had wondered if that dream would ever come true.

No one knew if I could have children. There were no guarantees that the existing part of the ovary would even produce eggs. The doctor had never seen a case like mine. The only advice he offered was "Don't wait too long to have a family." Since a female is born with a certain number of eggs, it was possible I might "run out" at any time. His words haunted me throughout high school and into college.

I met Ken at the end of my freshman year in college. His sparkling blue eyes and captivating personality soon won my heart, and we began to date steadily. I dreaded telling him about my surgery, because I knew he loved kids. But it would be unfair not to tell him. Would he back out of the relationship? I had to know.

One evening we went for a drive, and at the right moment the words tumbled out of my mouth before I could stop them. I told him about the tumor and the surgery and its results. I said we could stop dating if he wanted, since I knew how much having children meant to him. And for an awful moment I thought he might take me up on my offer as I watched the shock of my words filter through his eyes. Instead he bent down and kissed me, ending my worry.

We were married on August 9, 1987. I was still two years away from getting my teaching degree, so we decided to put our plans for a family on hold till then. However, after graduation God's leading took us to Guam as missionaries for two years. Then we moved to Texas, thinking we would settle there. Instead, we moved to

Kansas the following year, where we both found steady jobs in Wichita and purchased our first home.

At last we were ready to start a family. I could hardly wait! All my life I'd been praying for children. When the doctors discovered my tumor before it had encompassed *all* my ovaries, I knew God had worked a miracle, making pregnancy still a possibility. I could see His hand leading in every step of my life. I was certain He would answer my prayer for a baby!

Month after month passed. As each period began, tears rolled down my cheeks. Ken would take me in his arms and whisper, "Next month, honey."

A year and a half later my gynecologist said she had done all she could. We'd already taken several tests, and she had put me on Clomid, a fertility drug that forces one's body to release more eggs each month, thereby increasing the chance of pregnancy. However, the drug uses eggs faster, and no one knew how many eggs I had left. As the timing grew more important, I became desperate.

Then it was Christmas again. Even though I had experienced bouts of depression during the past year, it was hard to feel too bad as Christmas lights dazzled my eyes and brought joy to my heart. The snow sparkled like glitter outside my front room window as I sat down to write in my prayer journal.

Dear Father,

Your love is so amazing! I cannot comprehend it. Why do You love a sinner like me? You are so good and kind. Thank You for the many blessings in my life—my wonderful husband, a warm house, my dog, my parents, a good job, and Christmas. Thank You for answering my prayer about becoming pregnant with a healthy baby girl. It is my Christmas present from You, and I thank You for doing Your perfect will in our lives. I love You.

Missy

Even as I wrote the words, I wondered why I was thanking God for something He hadn't done. I was almost convinced I could never have children. Maybe I had no eggs left. In six weeks I would see a specialist, hoping he could tell me what my chances of becoming pregnant were. I was afraid our insurance wouldn't cover infertility treatments, and the potential of tremendous expense existed. But I had to know if I could have a child. My period was due in just a few days. Would God give me a baby—*now?*

I prayed so hard when I took the home pregnancy test. My fingers shook as I waited for the test result. Although I was only three days late for my period, I couldn't stand the suspense any longer. Finally, after one last prayer for strength, I opened my eyes.

"Positive!" I screamed in delight. "Praise God!" I cried over and over, tears streaming down my face. I knew He had worked a miracle. I felt awed and humbled by His mighty power and love.

I immediately went to the clinic to confirm the results with a blood test and gladly gave four tubes of blood. Then I went home to await the results. I wanted to be sure before I told Ken. The lab promised to call before 5:00.

Ken came home around 3:30 and got on the phone. Just when I thought he'd never get off, he hung up—and the phone rang. It was the clinic. I ran to the bedroom, barely able to breathe.

"How would a September baby sound to you?" the nurse asked.

"Does that mean I'm pregnant?" I stammered, incredulous.

"Yes. Your due date is September 2. We'll need to set up your first maternity visit."

I barely heard the rest. I was so excited. I had to tell Ken! As I hung up, he walked into the bedroom. I fell into his arms and whispered, "You're a father, honey!"

"No way!" Ken exclaimed, a slow smile spreading across his face.

"It's true!" I assured him. "I just got off the phone with the clinic."

His arms tightened around me as laughter and tears of joy flowed over us. He held me close. God had answered our prayers! My pregnancy was nothing short of a miracle.

We wasted no time in calling our family and friends. We wanted everyone to hear the miraculous story of our child. For Christmas I made my parents a card written from the baby's point of view. The card informed them that this present could not be wrapped in boxes or bows—it would arrive as a bundle of joy on September 2. My mother, who had waited seven years for grandchildren, had almost given up hope. But now the news brought great joy and excitement to my parents and grandparents. How I wished my grandfather, who had died from cancer just the year before, could have been there. Everyone was so happy!

At church the next week I told the pastor I had an announcement. In front of the entire church family I bravely told everyone about the miracle of my pregnancy and praised God for His goodness to Ken and me. We were flooded with good wishes and congratulations as the whole church rejoiced with us.

A few weeks later one of my good friends discovered that she too was pregnant. Her third child was due one month after ours. We immediately made plans to go maternity shopping (even though I wasn't showing yet). It was so much fun having a friend who shared the same enthusiasm.

As the weeks passed I began to plan the nursery around the theme "Jesus' Little Lamb" and began picking out wallpaper, buying stuffed toys, and subscribing to every baby magazine I could find. I picked out names, registered for Lamaze classes in the summer, and told my school superintendent that I was quitting my job so I could stay home with my baby the next fall. I began reading every book and article available on how to have a good pregnancy, determined to do my part. I started exercising, quit eating sugar, and changed my diet to be certain I was getting enough nutrients and vitamins. Every waking moment was spent in preparation for the birth of our child on September 2, 1994.

Then, during the second month of my pregnancy, I began experiencing some pain in my abdomen on my left side, in the area of my remaining fallopian tube and fragment of ovary. Friends had warned me about tubal pregnancies in which the fetus develops in the fallopian tube instead of the uterus. Everything seems normal until the baby grows too large for the tube. Then either the tube will explode, sometimes causing death to the mother, or the baby has to be aborted. The only symptom is pain in the abdomen.

To ease my concern, the doctor scheduled a sonogram at five and a half weeks. Ken and I followed a nurse down the hall to an examination room. My heartbeat quickened as I felt the cool, jellylike substance on my belly, and I riveted my gaze on the small black-and-white screen. All I could see were dark blobs.

I was almost afraid to ask where the baby was located,

knowing that if it were in a tube there was little hope of saving my child. Plus, a good chance existed that the tube would be damaged, eliminating the chance of any future pregnancy. Part of me was sure God would not allow this to happen after we had waited and prayed so long. Still, there was the pain.

Just as the suspense was about to overwhelm me, the doctor assured me the baby was in my uterus, just where it was supposed to be. The pain was most likely being caused by several ovarian cysts (a natural part of pregnancy, especially for those on fertility drugs). The cysts would disappear in time, the doctor said, and there was no need of worry.

I breathed a sigh of relief and squeezed Ken's hand. Then I saw the most astonishing sight: *our baby's heartbeat*—a small light on the screen, flashing in a steady rhythm, 120 beats per minute. The doctor said it would get faster as the baby grew. I was elated! It was the first glimpse of the tiny life I had waited for so long! The nurse handed me two pictures that I clutched tightly in my hand. I couldn't wait to show everyone my baby's first photos!

Everything was well. Gratitude flooded my heart. Why had I ever doubted? *Oh, Father, You are so good to me! Thank You, Lord. Thank You!*

Chapter 2

HEARTBREAK

This is what the Lord says: "I will give her peace that will flow to her like a river. . . . Like babies you will be nursed and held in my arms and bounced on my knees. I will comfort you as a mother comforts her child." Isa. 66:12, 13, NCV.

Two months later Ken and I waited once more in the doctor's office. We could hardly contain our excitement. We had *seen* our baby's heartbeat on the sonogram, but today we would *hear* it for the first time.

I flipped through magazines, dreaming about booties, strollers, and decorations for the nursery. Ken, who would never admit to being interested in baby things, peered over my shoulder, his eyes mirroring my anticipation.

I can't wait to hold you in my arms! I thought as I pictured my tiny bundle. *Six more months seems like an eternity, but at least I'll be able to hear you today. Oh, how I love you, my little one!*

Perhaps it was foolish to talk to an unborn baby, but I didn't care. I could almost feel pudgy fingers curling around mine, and hear the gentle coos as I swayed back and forth in the rocker. *A mother—I'm finally a mother!*

The nurse's call interrupted my reverie. We followed her to an examination room. As she turned to leave, I grinned at Ken. I knew what he was thinking. We were both glad that this time I was fine. I had no pain. My nausea had left me. I felt better than I had since I'd become pregnant. My energy had returned. No more mood swings or running to the bathroom every few minutes. I had survived the first three months! Both of us were relieved.

The nurse returned, carting a Doppler machine that would magnify the baby's heartbeat. The cold jelly was smeared on my abdomen and a metal wand slid over me. Almost immediately I heard a steady rhythm that sounded like the ocean beating on the rocks. *This was it. Our baby!* I looked over at Ken's elated face.

The nurse, however, didn't appear satisfied. She moved the wand back and forth, her puzzled expression the first warning that something was not right.

"That's the baby, isn't it?" I asked hopefully.

"No. That's *your* heartbeat—the baby's will be much faster. Don't worry, though," she said, "the doctor will be able to find it. That baby knows who's the boss!"

Fear's icy fingers suddenly ran down my back. I tried to chuckle, but it caught in my throat. Ken's hand tightened around mine. "It's OK, Miss. This probably happens all the time." Even as he said the words I knew he wasn't totally convinced.

Oh, God, I prayed desperately, *please, don't let anything be wrong.*

The doctor took her place next to the examination table. Again I heard a strong heartbeat, faster than before, but the doctor shook her head and ordered a sonogram. "We've got to see what's going on in there," she said.

Terror filled my eyes. *Wasn't this supposed to be the day Ken and I had anticipated for three months? How could this be happening?*

A black-and-white image materialized on the sonogram screen. The picture wavered. I could easily make out a black sack. Yes, there it was! The baby was coming into focus. I was amazed at how much it had grown since the last sonogram. Now I could make out a head and a body— maybe even legs. I wasn't sure. The baby seemed to be rocking in the circle.

So peaceful. Just as I'd seen it in my mind. For a moment I forgot reality, and the miracle of life swept over me. *How intricate. How perfect! I think it's looking at me!*

The doctor's voice jerked me back to reality. "This baby seems awfully small for three months. Check the chart, please. Could we have been mistaken on its age? Wait . . . I think I see it moving!" But she shook her head a few moments later and said, "No, I don't think it's the baby—it's your heartbeat. It just *appears* to be moving on the screen."

Desperately I searched for the rhythmic flashing. It *had* to be there! Besides, the baby was so much bigger than before.

Abruptly the doctor flipped off the machine. There was no heartbeat. Most likely the baby had stopped growing at two months. Something had gone wrong. No, there was no clue as to what it might have been. Probably genetic, though. Just to make certain, another sonogram would be scheduled by a different clinic with newer equipment.

"Are you all right?" The doctor's voice was thick with sympathy.

"It's OK," I stammered numbly.

"No," she replied. "It's not OK. It hurts. I'm really sorry."

Time stood still. Ken held me in his arms, my body engulfed in sobs. *Why, God, why?*

It seemed forever before the second sonogram was

taken. The receptionist immediately knew who I was by the expression on my face. She kindly ushered us into a private room where my sobbing would not disturb the other patients. Minutes ticked by as Ken tried his best to comfort me. Maybe our doctor had made a mistake. Maybe our baby was just small for its age. Maybe—I tried to pray, but the words kept getting jumbled in my mind.

At last a nurse ushered us into the examination room. Once again I felt the cold jelly being smeared on my abdomen. Once again I saw a black-and-white picture, this time much clearer than before. But I couldn't see the baby at all. The nurse assured me she was simply taking pictures of my abdomen. I sighed in relief.

Then there it was—a dark sack cradling a white form. I could see the shape now. A head. A body. Tiny buds for legs and arms. It looked so perfect! The baby seemed to be sleeping. I glanced up at the technician's face and saw a tear trickling down her cheek.

The tiny figure lay quietly without the slightest movement. No words were needed. My baby was dead.

By the time the doctor arrived, the picture on the screen was shaking violently from my sobs. The harder I tried to stop, the more the image shook. The doctor switched the picture, examining my uterus. When I had gained a bit of composure, he went back to the baby.

"I'm sorry." He shook his head sadly. "This is definitely a no-go pregnancy. Has your doctor talked to you about your options?"

What options? I wanted to scream. *How about saving my baby? Can't you do something?* But even as the thoughts crashed through my mind, I knew it was hopeless. No doctor in the world could revive a heartbeat in a fetus that had died a month before.

I looked into Ken's eyes for strength and comfort. A tear trickled down his cheek. His hand tightened around mine. "I've got to call your mother. She will wonder why you haven't come back to work."

I nodded numbly. The news would break her heart just as it had mine. Surely this was a nightmare! Anytime now I would wake up. But the minutes ticked by, and nothing happened. Nothing changed. Except the pain. It grew until its weedy fingers strangled the last strand of hope within me. I couldn't help staring at the image on the screen. I knew it would be my last glimpse of my precious baby that I would never hold or cuddle in my arms.

"You'll have another." The nurse's voice came from somewhere far away. "Take it from someone who knows. I lost my first one at eight weeks, just like you." I could see tears running down her cheeks and knew she understood, but it didn't help. Nothing could.

As we prepared to leave, I asked the technician softly, "Can I have a picture?"

"Sure. OK." She pushed a button and handed me a black-and-white portrait of my child. I clutched tightly to this tangible evidence that proved a baby had once grown inside me.

This tiny life had come so silently that I didn't even know it was there until two weeks after it began growing—and now it had left in the same way, four weeks before, about the same time my nausea had disappeared. Never had I considered the possibility of a miscarriage. This child was a miracle—a direct answer to prayer! Every day I had asked the Lord to make my little one strong and healthy, and every day I had trusted Him, certain that He would protect my baby if I did my part. I felt cheated one moment, and guilty the next. Could I have done more? Surely not. What did I do to deserve this?

Leaving the office, I stared at a mother and her baby in the waiting room. *Why, God, did You let this happen?* Even as the thought flashed into my head, I knew God was no more at fault than I was for my baby's death. Deep down I knew that.

As I walked out into the rain, a childhood memory trickled into my mind. I used to think God was crying when it rained. Maybe it was true. Perhaps our tears were mixing together before splashing onto the sidewalk.

When my doctor saw my face, she said, "I guess I must have been right about the baby."

I nodded, unable to speak.

"Then you have two choices. Either you can go home and wait for a natural miscarriage to occur, or I can perform a D & C [dilatation and curettage], which means that I will surgically scrape out the inside of your uterus."

I opted for the latter and asked if it could be done that day. She agreed to meet me at the hospital.

I suddenly realized I had only a few more hours left with this baby. Even if it was dead and my womb was its grave, at least it was close to me and was still mine. I wondered if the doctor would be able to tell whether it was a boy or a girl.

Somehow, I was sure it was a boy because of a dream I'd had the night before. I had never dreamed about the baby before. In my dream I gave birth to a boy. I was so disappointed, and I couldn't figure out why. Could it have been God warning me that something was wrong? There had been no other clue. No bleeding. No cramping. No pain. No anything. Everything seemed normal. It was just a regular doctor's appointment. Just a normal day.

"Oh, God," I cried out, "it's so easy to forget how wonderful 'normal' days are!"

Now I was going into surgery. I was going to have my baby early—*seven months* early. I could see the worry glistening in Ken's eyes as a nurse wheeled me toward the surgical ward. Somehow I had to comfort him, to ease the pain he was suffering silently. I managed a weak smile and promised, "Next time, honey, we'll do this right."

He nodded, and squeezed my hand.

Time stood still. After the surgery I couldn't remember anything about it. All I knew was that it was over. All over. My hopes and dreams of holding my baby had been ripped away, and now I was empty, completely empty. No feelings or emotions seemed to have survived.

Soon after I was wheeled into a hospital room to rest, my pastor came. Ken, my parents, and I listened as he read some texts from the Bible that should have been comforting. But they weren't. The pastor asked how this experience would affect my relationship with God. At first I wasn't sure; then one thought came clearly to my mind.

"Well, God gave His Son for me so—" The words choked in my throat. I now understood a little of what God had done in sacrificing His Son to save me. I hadn't even been able to spend time with my baby, and if it hurt this badly, what pain must God have felt?

My own suffering washed over me again. I felt as though I would be crushed under its load. Nothing could bring comfort. Suddenly all I wanted to know was if I'd see my baby again. Would I? I searched the pastor's face for even a tiny ray of hope. Embarrassed, he replied that the Bible didn't say. "But probably the baby would be as if it had never existed."

As if it had never existed! My indignation rose. Maybe God could forget about my baby, but I never would! I determined to study the subject out for myself. Surely the Bible could offer some kind of comfort and hope.

At last the pastor left. I was relieved to be alone. Part of me had died, been taken away forever. It was all a waste! God, *how could You be so unfair? It doesn't make sense that other mothers have the hope of seeing their babies again just because they lived long enough to be born. Don't You love the unborn child, too?* Tears stung my eyes as the pastor's words pierced my bleeding heart again. I determined to put the whole conversation out of my mind. For now, surviving was more important.

The next few days passed in a blur. I slept late, waking only long enough to realize that Ken was leaving for work. Every day I resisted the urge to run after him and beg him not to leave me. I felt so alone and empty. My life seemed to have no purpose or meaning. Friends called. I knew they meant well, but after breaking into sobs during the first conversation, I let the answering machine take my messages.

As one day slowly dragged into another, my curiosity grew. What *had* happened to my baby? What had gone wrong? Was it my fault? Was it God's? Are miscarriages common? What causes them? As the questions whirled around my mind like a tornado, I determined to find the answers.

I had to.

Chapter 3

THE MEDICAL MAZE
OF MISCARRIAGE

This is what the Lord says: "A voice is heard in Ramah, mourning and
great weeping, Rachel weeping for her children and refusing to be
comforted, because her children are no more." This is what the Lord says,
"Restrain your voice from weeping and your eyes from tears, for your
work will be rewarded," declares the Lord. . . . "So there is hope for
your future. . . . Your children will return." Jer. 31:15-17, NIV.

Except for the medical aspects, I could find very little information about miscarriages. I wondered if losing a baby was unusual for women my age. Maybe there was something wrong with me.

I learned that each year about 4 million women in this country give birth, and the total number of "risk" pregnancies ranges from 750,000 to more than 1 million.[1] While that is a lot of "risk" pregnancies, I still didn't know how many ended in miscarriage.

A 1990 study concluded that of the nearly 7.7 million pregnancies conceived in the U.S. that year, 2.6 million would end in miscarriage.[2] Each year in the United States alone approximately 600,000 to 800,000 women miscarry,[3] 80 percent before the end of the first trimester.[4] My pregnancy had ended at approximately eight weeks, so I fell into this 80 percentile. I was not alone—these losses touch nearly 1 million couples every year.[5]

Not only was one miscarriage fairly common, but even three or more occurred more often than I realized. "By very rough approximations, *one of every four women* has had a miscarriage; *one of every 300 has had three or more*. . . . In general, 10 to 15 percent of women with confirmed pregnancies miscarry. But this estimate refers only to miscarriages that occur after eight weeks of gestation."[6] If one takes into consideration losses that occur during the first few weeks of pregnancy, the statistics rise even higher.

In fact, more lives are lost in the first 20 weeks of pregnancy than are accumulatively lost in the next 65 years of life. Neither disease nor accident has claimed such a large number.[7] I was amazed. If the numbers are so high, why isn't there more research into what is causing these miscarriages? The United States is far behind other countries in its research. "The incidence of miscarriage and ectopic pregnancies has soared in the past decade. . . . Forty thousand babies die before their first birthdays, and the United States ranks sixteenth in infant survival rates, lagging far behind most industrialized countries."[8] With all our modern technology, surely we could do better than that!

Then in the midst of this discouraging information, one statistic brought some measure of comfort. When doctors discover a heartbeat, the chances for miscarriage go from about 20 percent to 3 percent.[9] Unfortunately, I had been one of those 3 percent who had seen a heartbeat, but still miscarried. Would the same thing happen again in my next pregnancy? Did I have any hope of carrying a baby to full term?

I learned that just because I had experienced one miscarriage, my chances of having another one were the same as the average woman's—one in four. However, for women older than 35 who have previously experienced one miscarriage and who have taken more than six months to become pregnant, chances increase to four in 10. When a woman has had two miscarriages, the possibility of miscarriage increases from one in four to one in three. However, even if the mother has experienced three or more miscarriages, she still has a 50-50 chance of carrying the baby full term.[10] Seventy to 80 percent of the women who have had even as many as three pregnancy losses do go on to bear healthy children. That is nearly a four-out-of-five success rate.[11]

Although some previous studies suggest that women who have miscarried three or more times have an 80 to 90 percent chance of repeated miscarriage, new research indicates that these women have no more risk than those who have miscarried only once. The research of Warburton and Fraser outlines these new findings as follows:

Previous Losses	Percent of Subsequent Losses
1	23.7
2	36.2
3	32.2
4	25.9

Instead of looking at the number of miscarriages one has had, researchers now consider two other factors as being more important: (1) whether or not the fetus was "chromosomally normal or abnormal," and (2) whether or not the woman has given birth to other healthy children.[12]

The age of the mother also affects the success rate of a pregnancy. Teenagers and women over 30 have more miscarriages than women who fall between these two categories in age.[13] Another study produced the following results:

Percent Miscarriage Rate	Women's Age
12	22
22	36
41	42

The rate of loss was nearly three and a half times as high for women over 40 as for their 20-year-old counterparts.[14]

At least I was still in the "ideal" age group for bearing children. My chances of having a full-term pregnancy were above average. One statistic was especially convincing: "Today more than 90 percent of women who've lost a baby before its birth go on to have healthy pregnancies and normal children."[15]

In addition to discovering the likelihood of miscarriage, I found that there were different kinds of miscarriages. To begin with, miscarriages (spontaneous abortions) refer to the loss of a fetus before the twentieth week of pregnancy.[16] These spontaneous abortions are divided into two types: threatened abortion and inevitable abortion.

Threatened abortion is a term used when a woman bleeds and cramps, but the cervix is still closed. The process could stop, and the pregnancy could continue. Half the women who bleed and cramp early in pregnancy do not miscarry.[17]

Inevitable abortion is similar to threatened abortion except that the bleeding continues, the cervix opens, and strong contractions occur. Unfortunately, at this point the pregnancy cannot be saved.[18]

If an inevitable abortion happens, either a complete, an incomplete, or a missed abortion will follow. A complete abortion takes place when the uterus has expelled all of the fetal and placental tissue.[19] An incomplete abortion, on the other hand, means that not all the tissue is removed from the uterus, and most likely surgery (dilatation and curretage) will be required.

The third type of miscarriage, a missed abortion, occurs when the fetus has died at least four weeks before being expelled in clumps of tissue or as a small embryo.[20] Usually labor will happen naturally in 90 percent of missed abortions, if allowed enough time. However, a woman can hemorrhage if she carries a dead fetus longer than four or five weeks, so labor may need to be induced.[21] Miscarriage in any form has a tremendous impact on the lives of all those involved, but experiencing a missed abortion is exceptionally devastating because of the stress incurred while waiting for the miscarriage to take place.

Even though I now understood the types of miscarriage, my heart longed to know why I had lost *my* baby. What are the causes of miscarriage? Several reasons include:

1. Major physical abnormalities.
2. A degenerating egg.
3. A gynecologic abnormality.
4. An "incompetent" cervix.
5. Fibroids, uterine adhesions, and scarring.
6. Previous abortions.
7. Progesterone deficiency.
8. Age.
9. Smoking, alcohol, and drugs.
10. Thyroid abnormalities.
11. Infections, chronic diseases, and immunologic mechanisms.

12. Surgery, serious diseases, or infections during pregnancy.

13. Prenatal diagnostic tests.

14. Environmental factors (toxic chemicals, radiation).

15. Poor nutrition.[22]

Another possible cause of miscarriage is polycystic ovaries. According to one study in the 1991 Birthright Annual Report, 80 percent of women who repeatedly miscarry have polycystic ovaries. Polycystic ovaries may be linked with higher than normal levels of luteinising hormone during the monthly cycle, something that has been significantly linked with causing miscarriages.[23] Polycystic ovaries, as well as other factors, have been found to contribute to both early and late miscarriages. However, within these two categories a few specific causes should be noted. For example, genetic errors are the main reasons for the three out of four early pregnancy losses that occur during the first trimester.[24] One source indicates that in early losses, a blighted ova (a chromosomal defect in the woman's egg) accounts for 20 percent of all miscarriages.[25] The embryo itself has a missing or extra chromosome in 50 to 60 percent of first trimester miscarriages, and about 20 percent of embryos have physical malformations that interfere with normal development.[26]

Since my own miscarriage had occurred during the first trimester, I gathered that it may have been caused by some form of genetic error. Fortunately, these random errors are not likely to repeat themselves, since the parents are usually not the determining factor. Research done at the University of Iowa suggests that in 98 percent of genetic studies, miscarriages are caused by the incorrect development of the baby. Only 2 to 10 percent of the studies indicate a problem with the parents.[27]

Early miscarriages, then, do not necessarily suggest that anything is genetically wrong with the parents. In fact, according to one study, women who miscarry seem to be more sensitive to problems in the growing fetus and have a lower incidence of children with deformities.[28]

On the other hand, difficulties in the baby's attachment to the placenta or uterus, structural problems in the uterus itself, or an incompetent cervix can cause miscarriages after the twelfth week.[29] However, women with these physical problems have more medical help available to them that may result in the ability to carry a baby to full term.

Although many reasons for miscarriage exist, several myths continue to prevail. Having sex, falls, and forbidden treats do not result in miscarriages.[30] Other factors that are not scientifically documented include: exercise and physical training during pregnancy, a previous miscarriage, emotional problems or nervousness, birth control pills used prior to conception, IUD (interuterine device) used prior to conception, and psychological shock.[31]

I was relieved to discover the truth about these myths, because I had worried that my exercise program or having intercourse had led to the loss of my baby. As I reviewed the list, I realized that I would need many medical tests in the future if I ever hoped to uncover the reason for my miscarriage. My desperation spurred me to make an appointment with Dr. Grainger, an infertility specialist at the Center of Reproductivity in Wichita, Kansas.

"Oh, God," I breathed, "could this appointment be the answer to my prayers for a healthy child?" I had no idea how we would ever be able to afford the infertility treatments. All I could do was pray about it.

---

[1]Dianne Hales and Timothy R. B. Johnson, M.D., *Intensive Caring:*

New Hope for High Risk Pregnancy (New York: Crown Publishers, Inc., 1989), p. 2.

[2] Laurie A. Rich, *When Pregnancy Isn't Perfect* (New York: Dutton, 1991), p. 6.

[3] Francine Toder, Ph.D., *When Your Child Is Gone: Learning to Live Again* (Sacramento, Calif.: Capital Publishing Co., 1986), p. 14.

[4] Rich, p. 6.

[5] Maureen Rank, *Free to Grieve: Healing and Encouragement for Those Who Have Experienced the Physical and Emotional Trauma of Miscarriage and Stillbirth* (Minneapolis: Bethany House Publishers, 1985), pp. 17, 18.

[6] Hales and Johnson, pp. 226, 227. (Italics supplied.)

[7] Pam W. Vredevelt, *Empty Arms: Emotional Support for Those Who Have Suffered Miscarriage or Stillbirth* (Portland, Oreg.: Multnomah Press, 1984), p. 7.

[8] Hales and Johnson, p. 2.

[9] Ellen Judith Reich, *Waiting: A Diary of Loss and Hope in Pregnancy* (New York: Park Press, 1992), p. 1.

[10] Vredevelt, pp. 86, 87.

[11] Rank, p. 140.

[12] Rank, pp. 87, 88.

[13] Rank, p. 20.

[14] *Ibid.,* p. 68.

[15] Hales and Johnson, p. 226.

[16] *Ibid.*

[17] Vredevelt, pp. 72, 73.

[18] *Ibid.*

[19] *Ibid.*

[20] *Ibid.*

[21] Rank, p. 87.

[22] Hales and Johnson, pp. 227-229; Vredevelt, pp. 75, 76.

[23] Karen Holford, *The Loneliest Grief* (Grantham, Eng.: Autumn House Publications, 1994), pp. 27, 28.

[24] Rank, p. 66.

[25] Holford, p. 27.

[26] Hales and Johnson, p. 227.

[27] Rank, p. 66.

[28] *Ibid.,* p. 86.

[29] Vredevelt, p. 75.

[30] Hales and Johnson, p. 230.

[31] Vredevelt, p. 76.

Chapter 4

FIRST REACTIONS

Be merciful to me, O God, be merciful to me! For my soul trusts in You; and in the shadow of Your wings I will make my refuge, until these calamities have passed by. Ps. 57:1, NKJV.

Even though I now understood more about my miscarriage, this knowledge brought little consolation. I longed to be alone, away from everybody. But at the same time I was desperately lonely. My entire body ached. All I wanted to do was cry, and sometimes I couldn't even do that.

By reading, I found that my moodiness could have been caused by the hormonal changes taking place within my body, and depression might continue anywhere from three to six months. According to some studies, new mothers have four to five times the risk of developing psychological illnesses during the first three months after delivery, and remain far more at risk for psychological disorders for six months after giving birth than do women in general.[1] Doctors estimate that 80 percent of women fight depression after a normal delivery, and these feelings are intensified when a mother has no baby to hold.[2]

This information reassured me that I was not going crazy. I had never experienced this type of depression before, and I was relieved to learn it was a normal symptom of grief.

Family and friends tried to offer encouragement and support through cards, phone calls, and visits. However, I soon realized that many people do not know how to express their sympathy. Some friends chose to avoid me altogether, because my grief made them uncomfortable. Other reactions to my miscarriage were anything but kind or helpful.

The most common response seemed to be "Well, you can always have another baby." The cruelty of this statement never failed to shock me. How could anyone think that one child could replace another? The very thought brought anger.

Others would advise, "Just have another as quickly as possible, and you'll forget about this one." Forget? Never! Try to have another one? We had already tried for a year and a half to have this one. Who knew how long the next one might take?

Someone else would quip, "At least you didn't lose a 'real' baby. It was just a bunch of cells." Why would anyone call my baby such a thoughtless name?

But the response I hated most was "God just never meant for that baby to be. His will is best, you know, because all things work together for good." God *never* "wills" a child to die! How dare anyone even insinuate such a thing? As for all things working out for the best, this may be true, but definitely not comforting at the time of loss.

My husband's response was also disheartening. He immediately threw himself into his work, seldom talked about the miscarriage, and seemed to distance himself from me. My tears must have made him feel uncomfortable, because instead of holding me in his arms as I expected him to do, he disappeared into another room, making some excuse as he left me suffering alone. When I needed him most, he seemed to be too busy to care. What I perceived to be indifference hurt me greatly.

It seemed as though everyone had forgotten so soon—everyone but me. The pain ate away at my heart until I screamed inside from the anger and hurt. My family, my friends—and even my husband—were tired of the subject. I felt deserted. More than anything, I needed to talk, now that I finally could—but no one seemed to be listening. I especially resented Ken. It was his support I valued and missed the most.

Going back to church (the same church where I had publicly announced my "miracle" pregnancy) proved to be a challenge. Inwardly I fought with feelings of shame, almost as if I had failed God and my church family by losing the baby.

Even though most people were kind and quick to share sympathy, I looked no one in the eye. Part of me wished I could run away to a place where no one knew that I had ever been pregnant. Again and again I felt forced to paint on a smile and comfort the one trying to comfort me. By the time church ended, I was physically and emotionally drained. Every ounce of my strength and willpower had been tapped to the limit. Tears threatened to overflow any minute.

Then, as I was trying to dash for the door, the friend who had become pregnant just weeks after I had blocked my way. We had never gotten a chance to go maternity shopping together. Now it would never be. I couldn't stand to look at her; she was just beginning to show. It wasn't fair—it was her *third* child. And they weren't even *trying* to get pregnant. Why couldn't it have happened to her instead of to me? Guilt washed over me as her look of empathy pierced my angry heart.

"I'm so sorry, Missy. I heard about your loss at prayer meeting, and I tried to call, but I couldn't reach you."

I had gotten her message; I just never returned her call.

"I wish there was something I could do . . ." Her eyes swam with tears as she reached for my hand.

I tried to answer, but the words choked in my throat. Turning abruptly, I ran out the door as the floodgates of my emotions broke loose.

In the following weeks I began reading Pam Vredevelt's *Empty Arms,* which helped me understand my anger better. I could relate so well with the author's feelings:

"I had so many *why* questions. Why us? Why our baby, when so many prayers had been offered on its behalf? . . . It seemed unjust. I was angry with the injustice, and I was angry with myself. Several of my friends were enjoying pleasant pregnancies. They were succeeding effortlessly. 'Why can't this body of mine do what it's supposed to do? I did everything Dr. Peterson ordered; why didn't things turn out for me?'"[3]

That was exactly how I was feeling. The more I tried to understand why, the more rage surged through my heart. Then, as quickly as anger would raise its ugly head, guilt would knock it down. *I have no right to question God. Anger is a sin, isn't it?*

Vredevelt answered this question a few pages later. When the Bible says, "In your anger, do not sin" (Eph. 4:26, NIV), it uses the word *orge,* which means "intense anger that comes as a reaction against sin or injustice."[4] Therefore, God must not consider being angry at injustice a sin!

When Jesus drove the merchants out of the Temple,

He displayed this type of righteous indignation (John 2:14-17). He was angry because His Father's house was being used as a marketplace instead of a holy meeting place of worship. If God showed this much emotion over the use of a building, how much more outrage must He feel when He sees an innocent life that He's created cut short through miscarriage! He must be able to understand my feelings of injustice, because He is angry too.

In fact, God can use my anger as a springboard to faith and a closer relationship with Him. According to one author, suffering builds patience and godliness and hope. Hurting refines faith so it will be strong and sure. A pain endured can lead to a special depth of friendship and identification with Christ.[5]

This realization was the first step toward dealing with my anger over losing my baby. However, I still wrestled with feelings of depression. I longed to talk to God face-to-face. If only I could feel His presence! But I felt nothing—nothing but bitterness and pain. Would it ever go away?

Anything could reduce me to tears—a trip to the mailbox, another baby magazine, a sympathy card, an announcement that a friend had just had her baby. *Everyone* seemed to be pregnant—my friends, strangers in the mall. Everywhere I looked I saw mothers and babies. Babies by the billions! Baby clothes, baby accessories, baby commercials on TV, baby billboards on the road, baby departments in the stores. Everyone had babies—everyone but me.

I had to escape. I had to find peace somehow. Just enough to get through another day, another minute, another second. Vredevelt says, "One of the worst responses you can have at this time is to ignore or try to bury your hurt. . . . If it's hard to talk to others, or if you don't feel as though there are many you can confide in, start a journal."[6]

Reaching under my coffee table, I pulled out my abandoned prayer journal and began to write. I wrote down everything that had happened—all of my thoughts and feelings. There was nothing to stop me. I wrote for hours. . . . No one understood. Not my husband or parents or church members. Everyone else could go on living normal lives. I had nothing left to live for. I had lost it all—my baby, my job, my life. I was treading water. Going nowhere. Did God care? Wasn't He supposed to be in control? Where was He, anyway?

I poured my frustrations and anger onto the pages until only a deep aching pain remained. I wanted answers from God. How did God view my unborn child? Did He think of my baby as a person, or just a bunch of cells? Maybe there was something in the Bible about miscarriages. I decided to look.

---

[1] M. Rank, *Free to Grieve,* p. 26.
[2] *Ibid.,* p. 25.
[3] P. Vredevelt, *Empty Arms,* pp. 27, 28.
[4] *Ibid.,* p. 29.
[5] Rank, p. 117.
[6] Vredevelt, pp. 20, 21.

Chapter 5

GOD'S VIEW OF THE UNBORN

You made my whole being; you formed me in my mother's body. I praise
you because you made me in an amazing and wonderful way. . . .
You saw my bones being formed as I took shape in my mother's body.
When I was put together there, you saw my body as it was formed.
All the days planned for me were written in your book before
I was one day old. Ps. 139:13-16, NCV.

I searched the Bible for comfort and assurance. The Psalms and Isaiah seemed especially soothing for someone who had experienced the loss of a child. Promises poured into my thirsty soul, and I found myself underlining verse after verse, amazed at how practical the Bible could be.

In chapter 26 Isaiah spoke poetically about miscarriages: "As a woman with child and about to give birth writhes and cries out in her pain, so were we in your presence, O Lord. We were with child, we writhed in pain, but *we gave birth to wind.* . . . But your dead will live; their bodies will rise. You who dwell in the dust, wake up and shout for joy" (verses 17-19, NIV).

I could especially relate to giving birth to wind—a perfect description of miscarriage. The promise I found in chapter 25 was such a comfort: "[God] will swallow up death forever. The Sovereign Lord will wipe away the tears from all faces" (verse 8, NIV). I couldn't wait for the day when death would be swallowed up forever, but what about now? Could God get me through today?

Another text jumped out at me. "You will keep in perfect peace [her] whose mind is steadfast, because [she] trusts in you" (Isa. 26:3, NIV). That was exactly what I needed—peace. Someone who understood my pain and sympathized with my suffering. I even found a text that referred to God crying "like a woman in labor" (Isa. 42:14, NKJV). I had never thought about God understanding the feelings of a mother so intimately. Yet I found such comfort in Isaiah 63:8 and 9 (NKJV), paraphrased in my own words, that assured me that Jesus understood *all* my trials and sorrows, because He also suffered while He was here on earth. Could it be that my loving Saviour was grieving with me, wishing to wipe away my tears?

A quote from the book *Free to Grieve* comments on the promise Jesus gave in Matthew 5:4: "When Jesus promised that those who mourn would be comforted, He laid down an inescapable prerequisite for receiving the deep, rich wonder of God's healing. To become a candidate for His comfort, you first must open yourself up to the pain of mourning. If you are a Christian, you share the life of One called 'a man of sorrows, and acquainted with grief.' Can you choose to be otherwise?"[1]

When I imagined Jesus wrapping His arms around my shoulders and crying with me over the loss of our baby, my heart melted. Miraculously, His tender love started pulling apart the strands of bitterness that had paralyzed my aching soul.

As I began giving my grief over to God, a burning desire for answers grew inside my heart. I remembered my pastor's words, "It will be as if the baby never were." My life had drastically changed since the loss of my child. It would *never* be the same! Surely a God who numbers the hairs on my head and sees the sparrow fall could not disregard my baby's death.

Through scientific evidence and Bible texts, I began discovering God's perception of the child in the womb. According to one medical source, "significant life" begins at conception. *Viable significant life* in the womb specifically exists during all of the first three months; that is, from the time of conception *fully meaningful life is present.* By the third week after conception the lobes of the brain are distinguishable. By the fourth week the head and face are recognizable and the heart starts to beat. During weeks five and six the eyes are identifiable and legs are putting on flesh and muscle. In the eighth week the embryo moves to the fetal stage, and in the following weeks its sex can be identified. The baby can begin to turn its head, squint, frown, make a fist, and even get the hiccups—all of this before the end of the first three months in the womb![2]

The Bible also supports the principle of life beginning at conception. Job asks, "Did not he who made me *in the womb* make them? Did not the same one form us both within our mothers?" (Job 31:15, NIV). And Isaiah declares, "Thus saith the Lord that made thee, and formed thee *from the womb*" (Isa. 44:2). These texts indicate God has an active part in the physical development of the embryo.

God evidently considers a person's lifetime to extend from conception until death. He told Samson's parents that "the child shall be a Nazirite to God *from the womb to the day of his death*" (Judges 13:7, NKJV). Physical life, therefore, does not begin at birth. In God's eyes it begins at conception and continues until that person dies.

Shortly before discovering I was pregnant, I learned Psalm 139 as a song. The words grew to mean more and more to me as my pregnancy proceeded. When I miscarried, I went back and studied this psalm (NKJV) in detail, using my computer to look up the Hebrew definitions of the important words (shown in brackets). This is what I discovered:

Verse 13: "You [Jehovah] formed [God originating, creating, redeeming His people] my inward parts [seat of emotion and affection]; You covered [wove together] me in my mother's womb [belly, abdomen]."

Verse 14: "I will praise You, for I am fearfully [with astonishment and awe] and wonderfully [distinct, separate, distinguished] made; marvelous [wonderful, surpassing, extraordinary] are Your works, and that my soul [living being] knows very well."

Verse 15: "My frame [power, bones, might] was not hidden from You, when I was made in secret, and skillfully wrought [woven] in the lowest parts of the earth."

Verse 16: "Your eyes saw my substance [embryo, fetus], being yet unformed. And in Your book [record book of God] they [my members] all were written [recorded, enrolled]."

In this psalm God records the baby's physical features in "His book." One writer compares this physical record to the DNA that is present in every human cell. Speaking of Psalm 139:15 and 16, Jack Hayford suggests that as recently as the 1950s two biologists won the Nobel Prize upon discovering the secrets of DNA, the spiraling double helix within the cellular structure of the human body, which holds in coded form the details of every aspect of each person's physical potential.[3] As a result of this scientific discovery, Hayford concludes, "even in the smallest collection of cells formulating the tissue of a miscarried child, the encoded message of its physical development and appearance-to-be are already present."[4] God sees a unique individual, not just a bunch of cells.

If God could attend to such physical detail in the unborn child, surely He loves and cares about that baby as much as I do—and more! God says, "Can a woman forget her nursing child, and not have compassion on the son of her womb? Surely they may forget, *yet I will not forget you.* See, I have inscribed you on the palms of My hands; your walls are continually before Me" (Isa. 49:15, 16, NKJV). God never forgets one of His precious children! He loves the child so much that He writes down all his days in a book (Ps. 139:16, NIV). Even more intimately than a mother, the Lord remembers and loves the unborn!

God has a reason for the unborn's existence. "The days [lifetime] fashioned [be predetermined, preordained] for me when as yet there were none of them. How precious [esteemed, prized, valuable, costly, appraised] also are Your thoughts [purposes, aims, thoughts] to me, O God! How great [vast, numerous] is the sum of them" (Ps. 139:16, 17, NKJV).

According to this psalm, God has a plan, a purpose, for each child's life. Just as He weaves together nerves, bone, muscle, and tissue, He also sees the child's future before it even happens. God beholds the unborn baby much as an artist pictures a beautiful statue from a simple clump of clay. He highly values the child, and His plans for its life are too numerous to count. How tragic it must be for the Lord when His purposes are thwarted through miscarriage or infant death!

Other Bible prophets state that God has a plan for the unborn's life. Isaiah claims Jesus was formed in His mother's womb to be a servant of God (Isa. 49:5, NIV). Samson is called a "Nazarite unto God from the womb" (Judges 13:5). In both texts God's purpose for the life of the individual began in the womb. Likewise, in Jeremiah 1:5, God Himself declares, "Before I formed you in the womb I knew you, before you were born I set you apart; I appointed you as a prophet to the nations" (NIV). According to Hayford, this verse illustrates that God's purpose for people is already in force—in His mind and intent—while they are yet in the womb.[5] Just as God ordained Jeremiah as a prophet before birth, so today God has a plan for the unborn child's life.

God discerns the future of the unborn and knows whether or not they will accept Him. Speaking of the house of Judah, God says, "I knew that you would deal very treacherously, and were called a *transgressor from the womb*" (Isa. 48:8, NKJV). Paul argues that God knows the future of the unborn before they do "anything good or bad" and cites Jacob and Esau as examples (Rom. 9:11-13, NIV). God declared that "the older will serve the younger" (verse 12) and "Jacob I loved, but Esau I hated" (verse 13). God knew the outcome of both men's lives from the time of their conception. In fact, He told their mother, Rebekah, that "two nations are in your womb, and two peoples from within you will be separated; one people will be stronger than the other, and the older will serve the younger" (Gen. 25:23, NIV).

Because God knows the end from the beginning, He can predict the future of the unborn. What's even more amazing is that God knows the unborn baby by name! In a prophecy referring to the birth of Jesus, Isaiah says, "The Lord hath called me from the womb; *from the bowels of my mother hath he made mention of my name*" (Isa. 49:1). If God knows the future of the unborn and has plans for their lives, He must love them dearly—enough to know each one individually, by name. What amazing love!

Besides knowing the unborn child intimately, God can fill the babe with His Holy Spirit while he or she is still in the mother's womb, just as He did for John the Baptist. In Luke the angel of the Lord proclaims, "He [John] will be great in the sight of the Lord, and shall drink neither wine nor strong drink. He will also be filled with the Holy Spirit, *even from his mother's womb"* (Luke 1:15, NKJV). John was filled with the Holy Spirit from the time of conception. When Elizabeth greeted Mary, the baby in her womb "leaped for joy," and she was filled with the Holy Spirit (Luke 1:44, NIV). Even before his birth John experienced joy from being in the presence of his unborn Saviour. While still in the womb he recognized his Creator.

Applying John's experience in the womb, Hayford states, "Let no one say the unborn are without spiritual sensitivity or purpose. . . . The small human mass within the womb is already tuned to the Spirit of his or her Maker."[6] And although Jesus had just been conceived, He is spoken of as "the Lord" and "God my Savior" (Luke 1:46, 47, NIV). Mary sings a song of praise to Jesus, even though He is but an embryo at this time.

Hayford makes another interesting point about the timing of these events. We are explicitly told that a child has been conceived in Mary's womb. In addition to giving the exact chronology of the event, the child is spoken of as present, as alive, and as "the Lord," no less a person for being a embryo.

Mary stayed with Elizabeth, who was in her sixth month of pregnancy, until the birth of Elizabeth's baby. "In other words, when Elizabeth was filled with the Holy

Spirit and prophesied on Mary's arrival—'the child in your womb is the Lord'—Mary was only a matter of a few days into *her* pregnancy."[7]

Therefore, Elizabeth, who was "filled with the Holy Ghost," and Mary, who conceived by the Holy Spirit, both affirmed that Christ was their Lord and Saviour from the first moments of conception. Through their example, one can see the value God places on the unborn child. He does not wait until birth to regard the unborn as living, spiritual human beings. He proclaims them His children from the womb.

As I read these texts my heart swelled with gratitude for a God who loved my baby and me. God treasured my baby so much that He carefully installed every physical detail into its cells. He knew whether my baby would have brown, blue, or hazel eyes. He could see its hair color, and He even knew how many hairs there would be.

In her summary of Psalm 22:9 and 10, Vredevelt declares, "My God is also my baby's God. . . . 'Yet you brought me out of the womb; you made me trust in you even at my mother's breast. From birth I was cast upon you; *from my mother's womb you have been my God.*'"[8]

That same God was also my child's God—from the first day that that baby was placed in my womb. I was not the only one who had missed the joy of watching this little one grow. The Lord Himself had lost part of His family, for this tiny being was a priceless prince or princess of the King! God and I were partners in pain, suffering from sin.

Somehow I could no longer blame God for my miscarriage. I knew that even though He has the ability to destroy evil, He respects the power of choice. It was Satan, not God, who chose to rebel against his Maker. It was Adam and Eve, not God, who chose Satan as the ruler of this world. It was I, not God, who chose to sin. That is why humanity suffers—because sin has not been totally destroyed. Oh, it has been overcome at the cross and will be totally eradicated at Jesus' second coming, but today its ugly effects still haunt us.

Nevertheless, God remains in control. Sometimes He steps in and prevents the consequences of sin from touching our lives; sometimes He does not. We don't always know the reasons—we only know that He loves us and can see the beginning from the end (Rev. 22:13).

Perhaps one way to understand God's viewpoint is to realize that we are in a battle. The plain fact is that some of us get wounded; others die. That is the result of this war, this great controversy between Satan and Christ. If God chose to heal His every child, Satan would scream, "Unfair!" So that all will see the terrible effects of sin, God allows everyone to be touched by it in some way. It may be a miscarriage, the loss of a spouse, a deadly disease, a bankruptcy, a divorce, a murder. All suffer because of sin. No one escapes. Not even God—perhaps He suffers most of all. He's the only one who has remedied the situation, yet He receives the most blame.

I bowed my head in shame. *Oh, God! I'm sorry I blamed You for my pain. We're both suffering, aren't we?* And somewhere in the silence, a tear echoed mine.

Months later I received a package from my former first-grade teacher. I had grown to love her so much through the years that I thought of her as my grandmother. Only months earlier she had sent me a crocheted baby blanket. Now I discovered a letter and an audiotape inside the wrapping paper. She had heard about my miscarriage. With tender words of comfort she poured out her heart to my thirsty soul. Ever so gently she reminded me of the great controversy between Christ and Satan and encouraged me to listen to the sermon she'd recorded on the tape, "God's Honor Roll."

Perhaps, she wrote, *you have been called to be a part of this honor roll that will suffer for Christ's sake and stand true for Him. Then when others say, "I would have served You, Lord, if You would have just saved my baby," there will be a witness for Christ who can stand and declare, "I lost my child too, but God gave me peace and strength to endure, and now I have not only my baby, but all of heaven! Praise God, for He is just and good!*

Her letter touched my heart. *God's Honor Roll . . .* the words tumbled around in my mind. *O Lord,* I prayed silently, *help me be worthy of such a title.*

---

[1] M. Rank, *Free to Grieve,* p. 46.

[2] Jack Hayford, *I'll Hold You in Heaven* (Ventura, Calif.: Regal Books, 1990), p. 30.

[3] *Ibid.,* p. 77.

[4] *Ibid.*

[5] *Ibid.,* p. 52.

[6] *Ibid.,* p. 54.

[7] *Ibid.,* p. 32.

[8] P. Vredevelt, *Empty Arms,* p. 36.

Chapter 6

AFTERMATH

*Casting all your care upon Him, for He cares
for you. 1 Peter 5:7, NKJV.
He heals the brokenhearted and binds up
their wounds. Ps. 147:3, NKJV.*

Although knowing that God understood the struggles I was experiencing brought me much encouragement, there were still days when I fought depression. I felt fat. I hated to look into the mirror. The extra pounds I had so happily gained did not come off as easily as I had put them on. Gaining a bra size was one great benefit of being pregnant I had particularly enjoyed. Now my breasts seemed to have almost totally disappeared. I tried to work out, but even that left me depressed because I hated exercising, and the little weight I lost seemed only to be from my chest and not my waist. I was sure I'd never look "normal" again.

However, my appearance was not nearly as big a problem as paying the bills. I dreaded going to the mailbox. If it wasn't a baby magazine or a sympathy card, it was a hospital bill. I had never dreamed how expensive a miscarriage was. The doctors' visits and hospital bills cost almost as much as a normal delivery. Then just when I thought I had everything paid, another bill would arrive. The radiology department. The lab. The gynecologist. The hospital. The pathologist. I thought it would never end.

My burning anger finally erupted like Mount St. Helen's when I discovered a bill for "the study and disposal of fetal tissue." *What had they done to my baby?* I could almost see a lab technician dissecting my child like a frog in a biology class. How dare they! And now they wanted me to *pay* them? Never! After explaining my situation to the unfortunate nurse who took my call, I discarded the bill.

Having a miscarriage affected every aspect of my life. Often I found myself in circumstances that released a wave of emotion. I once lost my Social Security card and went downtown to get another one. While standing in line, I glanced up to see a woman with a bulging stomach (she was probably nine months pregnant) standing in the next line. Before I could look away, I noticed large black letters on her maternity top: "S— Happens," it proclaimed, and a big arrow pointed to her stomach.

Instantly I felt my face flush red and my hands clench into fists. *How could you ever wear such a thing?* I wanted to scream. I hated her, and I didn't even know her. She had the one thing I desired above all else, and she didn't even want it. Tears sprang to my eyes. I grabbed my new Social Security card and ran back to my car.

Another time I was shopping with a friend when we ran across some assorted sale items. As I turned around, she held up some tiny overalls and exclaimed, "Oh, aren't these just darling! I think I'll get them for one of the church members who just had her baby. What do you think?"

The expression on my face must have told much more than the words that caught in my throat, because she quickly stammered, "I hope this won't bother you."

I shook my head. She seemed relieved and went back to her shopping. I felt as though I had just been slapped with a cold wet rag. Although I tried to act as though nothing had happened, the rest of my day was spoiled.

~ ~ ~

Weeks passed, and the day I had been dreading quickly arrived. I had to go back to the women's clinic for my checkup, the same clinic where only a few weeks before I had been so eager to hear my baby's heartbeat. Ken had come with me then. Desperately I wished he were here now.

As I sat in the waiting room, I tried not to notice the pregnant women. I tried not to stare at the toddlers playing cars on the floor. I tried not to see the pictures of infants on the walls and the teddy bears romping across the brightly colored wallpaper.

But I saw it all. And inside I felt nauseated and wondered why I couldn't wait in a different room. Searching frantically for a distraction, I glanced down at some magazines. Baby pictures stared back at me. Perhaps the same ones I had looked at an eternity before . . . I felt like a caged animal, fighting to escape the pain.

A nurse called my name. She smiled. "How are you doing?" I could hear the sympathy in her voice, and tears almost spilled over. She led me to an examining room—not the same one I had been in before, but we walked by it. Floods of memories swept over me. The excitement. The anticipation. The worry. The tragedy. It was all still there—just a few doors down the hall.

The appointment lasted about five minutes. After checking my uterus, the doctor said I looked fine. Unfortunately, I didn't feel that way. The nurse ushered me to the receptionist's desk, where the secretary handed me yet another bill. I took it and fled to the elevator.

It was over. I had made it. No sobbing. No breakdown. For a moment I was almost proud of myself. Then the elevator door opened, and there stood a mother with her newborn baby. She smiled as she glanced down at the sleeping child in her arms before hurrying by to get to her doctor's appointment. The pent-up dam of grief exploded, and my shoulders shook as tears crashed down my cheeks. I hardly noticed people's curious stares as I rushed into the elevator, then out to my car.

Maybe I hadn't been so brave or strong after all, but I had survived.

Chapter 7

REASON TO GRIEVE

*You have kept record of my days of wandering. You have stored my
tears in your bottle and counted each of them. Ps. 56:8, CEV.
The Lamb in the center of the throne will be their shepherd. He will
lead them to streams of lifegiving water, and God will wipe
all tears from their eyes. Rev. 7:17, CEV.*

Weeks passed slowly. No one offered sympathy anymore. Even close friends and family avoided the subject. Again and again I got the impression that since my baby had never been born, I had no right to grieve very long. After all, it wasn't like losing a "real" baby. I should have already recovered. But as the days stretched into months, my heart still ached. It was as though a part of me were dead, and no matter how hard I tried, I couldn't go back to "normal." What was wrong with me?

I turned once again to my library books searching for an answer, any answer. Mourning has a timetable that we cannot always control, I learned. According to Judith McCoyd, "Grief is grief. It has its own scale and it's not related to length of gestation. While there may be differences in how people grieve, you don't have to grieve less if you lost your baby at 12 weeks' gestation rather than at two days after full-term birth."[1]

These words brought encouragement to my aching soul. I didn't have to feel foolish about grieving for my unborn child! Even though I had never held my baby, my heart was attached to it. And when I miscarried, I felt as though a part of me had been ripped away. Were these feelings normal? Evidently. Psychologists have found that the length of time a fetus or infant survives has no correlation with maternal grieving. Mothers whose babies die before birth may mourn as intensely as those whose infants live for several months.[2] One writer claims that "some psychotherapists believe that losing a baby who never lived may, in its own way, be harder than mourning for a specific individual."[3]

This made sense to me. When I thought of my child, I couldn't picture its face or hear its cry or hold its tiny hand. I had no mental image of my baby, and this emptiness only added to my pain.

Society does little to support a woman who has miscarried. Because few view the miscarriage as a death, the mother is left feeling guilty for grieving. A Clemson University study done on mourning mothers found that although feelings of anger and bitterness were more commonly expressed by mothers whose children died after birth, women who miscarried or delivered stillborn babies felt guilt and failure more intensely.[4] Because they don't understand the mother's feelings, few take time to encourage or empathize. As time passes, most forget or consider the miscarriage just a little "mishap." Shamefully, the mother is left to struggle alone with the pain.

Since I had no other children, most people didn't consider me a mother. At one Mother's Day church service I attended, mothers in the congregation were honored by receiving a carnation. When the girl with the flowers saw me, she hesitated, then handed me one and said, "Well, I *guess* you can have one." I didn't know whether to accept or refuse it. A few minutes later a part of me wished I had declined as I walked painfully past the curious stares of the crowd. However, I *was* a mother, no matter what anyone else thought.

According to sociologists Larry Peppers and Ronald Knapp, maternal love, whatever its source, reaches deeply into the very earliest stages of pregnancy, and attaches itself firmly to the growing infant. Loss of that infant is a very real experience, and the mother's grief over that loss can become oppressive.[5] What people do not realize is that for the mother this infant has been a part of her since conception. She has come to know it in a way that no one else has. Her breasts ache to nurse and her arms long to hold her lost infant. She literally feels empty, weak, and insecure; a very real and significant part of her has died.[6]

The emptiness of my arms taunted my heart's burning desire for children. So few understood that kind of pain.

The mother is not the only one who suffers from the loss of a child. Many don't realize the extent of the father's grief after a miscarriage. My husband recounted his feelings this way:

"I was disappointed. Even though our miscarriage affected Missy more than it did me, I still felt a great sense of sadness and, most of all, I wondered if we'd ever have a baby, if what I'd dreamed for would ever happen."

Another husband stated that his reaction to the miscarriage was a state of shock. He felt "numb, helpless, and out of control. I never saw or felt the baby. I had no personal attachment to the child; my attachment was with my wife. I tried to comfort her, but I didn't know what to say. I felt as though I was a third person, looking in on the grief because I was not physically affected by the miscarriage. Since society doesn't recognize this type of loss, it was easy to push it aside. Ignore it. Pull in my feelings. Not let anyone know what had happened."

A third husband said he felt "traumatized" by his wife's grief and had many "unanswered questions." However, he could not verbalize his feelings to his wife (which made her think he was apathetic). Instead, he poured out his sorrow on his computer, and there, in the privacy of his office, he broke down and cried. "I couldn't cry in front of my wife. I couldn't talk about it. I couldn't even read her what I wrote. I guess I felt that men were supposed to be strong and silent. Now I believe men need to get in touch with their feelings and share them with their wives, if possible."

The reactions of these three men echo the description of emotional upheaval recorded by one author. "The loss of a child produces irrevocable change. You can never go back to living the same life, try as you will, because of the changes produced by your loss. It is as if you have a large jigsaw puzzle that you laid out, only to find that one or more key pieces were missing. The puzzle can never be complete in this state. It isn't even possible to fill the space with anything else. If you attempt to keep the whole form or shape intact, then the missing pieces will always be most noticeable. So it is with your life. Unless it can be changed or reworked to minimize or fill in the spaces, then the loss will always be central."[7]

Since both husband and wife are deeply affected by the loss of a baby in their own unique ways, each spouse must show understanding toward the other's grief. Just because my husband didn't spend hours crying and expressing his feelings as I did didn't mean he wasn't hurting the same as I was. Although I needed Ken for support, he needed to be left alone for survival.

One book I read helped me understand this paradox a little better: The "overdependent" is a person who leans on another for emotional strength to the point of suffocation, while the "super independent" withdraws and wants to be alone.[8]

I was definitely an "overdependent." My expectations were too great. Instead of leaning on Christ for my strength, I had smothered Ken. Once I realized that my husband needed time to grieve in his own manner, I was able to give him more freedom. In return, he gave me the support I needed, and no longer seemed to push me away.

Another common reaction when experiencing the death of a baby is to reevaluate one's own life. "The loss of a child is so profound that it shakes the foundation of life. It batters beliefs and forces a confrontation with values. It strikes at the heart of life."[9]

I found myself looking at life very differently than I had before my miscarriage, especially concerning my views of dying. My eyes were suddenly opened wide to the startling reality that I could lose my loved ones at any moment. I became afraid for Ken go to work, fearing he might be killed on the job. I worried about my mother driving an hour to work each day because of the chance she might be in a car accident. Even though these fears were unreasonable, they haunted me for a short time following my miscarriage. Since I had never experienced death face-to-face, I was awed by its power.

I had nightmares about losing my family, not only by death, but by other means as well. I dreamed several times that Ken wanted a divorce, and that there was nothing I could do to change his mind. Unconsciously I feared losing everyone I loved. Never had I felt so helpless, so miserable, so desperate. My whole world seemed out of control. Even though in reality Ken had no intentions of leaving me, I still could not control my fears. And because of these fears, I began to realize the significance of making the most out of the time I had with my family.

"Death affords those who are left an opportunity to reevaluate everything. And though we would give all we have to defer that opportunity, it exists anyway. It allows us to see the flimsiness of our expectations, to realize there is no expectation without disappointment; it allows us the possibility of being more sensitive, more vulnerable, to let others support us, and to notice the integrity and love often left unobserved in life's fast pace."[10]

Since my world had come to a sudden stop during the miscarriage, I had time to think. I began appreciating my marriage and my friends and family more than I had previously. What if one of them *did* die? Would I have said all I wanted? Would they know how much I love them? These questions made me more determined to show my loved ones how much I cared. Understanding the fragility of life helped me begin the process of coping with death.

As time passed I realized I must take deliberate actions in order to work through my grief. The first step of recovery is *to acknowledge and to express my sorrow openly*. The death of my child was real to me, even if others may not have realized it. Although tears often flowed, I was comforted to find that "losing a child is one of the most emotionally intolerable experiences imaginable. The healthiest response . . . would be a total letting go: openly grieving, uncontrolled display of feelings, and a willingness to let the feelings wash over you until, like the tide, they recede in intensity."[11]

As I cried, the anger, fear, and frustration seemed to diminish, leaving a sense of peace. Even though I felt empty from the loss, I could sense strength returning. Healing emerged from my tears.

Fortunately, I didn't try to block my grief, which can be psychologically and physically detrimental. According to Edward Martin, "frozen grief" (a term for repressed or blocked sadness) is the most dramatic of the abnormal bereavement reactions. If grief is not openly expressed, it can cause physical disease, especially in the intestinal tract, which seems to be the weakest link in the body's defenses against emotional assaults.[12] It has been found that 75 percent of colon ulcers are linked to grief situations. Surprisingly, physical symptoms may not surface in a person experiencing frozen grief until years after the death of the loved one.[13]

Another study, specifically highlighting the denied grief of mothers who had miscarried, echoes these findings. Peppers and Knapp often saw the consequences of a grief denied, especially in the case of miscarriage. "Grief may be openly expressed, or it may remain hidden and unexpressed in feelings of guilt, bitterness, and sadness. The overt expression of grief can be highly beneficial to the person who has experienced a loss. Hidden grief, on the other hand, may remain unresolved; furthermore, it can be detrimental to the physical, mental, and social well-being of the grieving individual."[14]

The second step of recovery is *to recognize that the death of my child has had a tremendous impact on my life.* I must choose whether this impact will be positive or negative. In her book *When Your Child Is Gone* Francine Toder states, "The loss of a child creates upheaval in one's life in a very poignant way. This loss separates the past and the future very clearly, as if cut by a knife. The effect of this division may be startling change, but also startling growth."[15]

My response to the tragedy was vital to overcoming my grief. I had to choose how my baby's death would shape my life. I could either cling to my anger and pain and let it destroy me, or I could release my grip and replace my anger with love and concern for others who were suffering. I could only pray that God would help me grow through the grieving process instead of becoming bitter.

Along with realizing the tremendous impact the tragedy has had on one's life, it is also an important part of the second step of grieving to progress through five distinct stages. According to Dr. Elisabeth Kübler-Ross, these stages of grieving consist of denial and isolation, anger, bargaining, depression, and acceptance of the loss.[16] A person may spend different amounts of time at a certain level, but most seem to experience some symptoms of each.

Stage 1: Denial and isolation. When the doctor first told me I was going to miscarry, I had a hard time accepting my baby's death. Perhaps the sonogram was wrong. Maybe my baby was just small for its age. After all, doctors had been wrong before. When the truth became too obvious to deny, my heart cried out to escape from the pain, to crawl into a dark cave where no one could remind me that only days before I had carried a baby.

Stage 2: Anger. I lashed out at God, my husband, my doctor, and myself. Why did this have to happen to me? It wasn't fair! Why couldn't Ken be more supportive? Why hadn't the doctor caught this earlier when there still might have been time to do something? What is wrong with this body of mine, anyway? I can't even do something even a 14-year-old teenager can do! Any female ought to be able to carry a baby to full term; why can't I? My fury threatened to engulf me.

Stages 3 and 4: Bargaining and depression. As the days turned into months, I began bargaining with God to give me another baby. I would do anything if only He would grant this one request. But as another period would begin, I would sink deeper into despair. Nothing mattered. My life was ruined. I might never get pregnant again. The very thought of spending the rest of my life childless crushed my heart and hope. I spent hours crying and mulling over the tremendous loss of all my childhood dreams that seemed to lie shattered at my feet.

Stage 5: Acceptance. I desperately hung on to God, my husband, my family, and my friends. I needed a listening ear, a warm hug, a reassuring voice. Even though the pain remained, it became more and more bearable. Instead of being totally overwhelmed with grief, I began noticing the world around me again—the birds singing, the flowers blooming. Little things, but each one meant so much. They were promises to me, promises that one day I might even laugh again.

The third step of recovery is *to memorialize one's miscarried child*. This step incorporates the first two steps, because it not only is a concrete expression of one's sorrow, but also allows the pain to be channeled into a positive outlet. One of the most therapeutic activities I remember doing through the long days that followed my miscarriage was making a scrapbook of my baby. Often a tangible way of remembering the miscarried baby is helpful to grieving parents. One book suggests creating a quiet memorial of your own, something tangible and physical, to mark your child's existence.[17]

I purchased a baby book and began filling its pages with memories:

- ✧ My positive pregnancy test.
- ✧ My first sonogram pictures of the baby at five and a half weeks.
- ✧ The card I made for my parents that announced the baby's due date.
- ✧ The valentine I made Ken, congratulating him on being a father.
- ✧ Snapshots of my parents' reaction to the news that they were going to be grandparents.
- ✧ My hospital band when I went in for my D & C.
- ✧ The cards sent from friends and family.
- ✧ The last sonogram pictures before my surgery.

All these items were lovingly arranged across the pages. In a way, I was closing a chapter of my life. It was an ending. A completion. A way to say goodbye.

I soon discovered that many mothers who had experienced a miscarriage bought or made some sort of tangible memorial for their child. One mother purchased a ceramic figurine of a newborn to add to her doll collection. Another cross-stitched a picture in remembrance of her loss. I planted a rosebush in my backyard that I dedicated to my precious baby. Other concrete ways of dealing with grief could include:

- ✧ Purchasing and displaying booties or a special baby picture in the baby's bedroom.
- ✧ Writing a poem to the lost child.
- ✧ Donating a picture to a children's department or mother's room in a local church.
- ✧ Marking and dating Bible texts that have been especially comforting.
- ✧ Buying a bouquet of flowers on the date of the miscarriage.

A variety of means for turning grief into something concrete exist if a mother uses her imagination. One of my close friends shared a letter she had written to her miscarried baby. She says this simple exercise not only brought comfort, but allowed her to work through the grieving process by expressing her feelings in a written memorial to her lost child. With her permission, I am sharing it.

Dear Destiny Joy,

You'll never know the excitement you brought into our family when we found out about you. We called you our little surprise package from heaven—a special gift from God—and we couldn't wait for you to arrive. As soon as we discovered you were on the way, we told everyone about you: your grandparents, aunts, uncles, friends— even all the church members. Everyone was excited for you to come.

You were to have arrived in February (your due date was the twenty-fifth). What better time than the month of love! You were conceived in love from your mommy and daddy. You were an expression of our love, and we couldn't wait to see you. We had so much love to give you.

As I began to think about your coming, I started to get all kinds of ideas about how I was going to decorate your nursery. Daddy and I cleaned out an extra room upstairs just for you. My friend gave me a beautiful white bassinet and all kinds of little girl clothes. I even started getting my maternity clothes ready, so I would have things to wear as you grew bigger. We told your big brother about your arrival and about how much fun the two of you would have playing together, since you would have been only 20 months apart.

But then on July 28 we lost you. I can't even begin to describe the pain and emptiness I felt inside when you were gone. I hadn't even gotten to see you yet. I hadn't even heard your heart beating (though it had been for several weeks).

I miss you, little one. Even now, as I write this letter, I miss the kicking and squirming you should be doing inside of me right now. I feel empty without you and cheated that I didn't get to see you or watch you grow up.

Not long ago I saw a little girl at a playground. She asked me to help her swing. As I watched her play, I noticed her big eyes and beautiful hair, and I couldn't help wondering if you would have looked like that. I asked her name, and she told me it was Destiny. That's your name, little one—she had your name! Maybe that was God giving me a little glimpse of what you may have been like.

We named you Destiny Joy so that every time we thought of you we would be reminded of the joy we are destined to have in heaven when we will raise you in a perfect world. We also named you Joy because you brought such joy into our lives when you were here.

I miss you so much! But I am comforted by knowing that I will meet you again when Jesus comes. I can't wait to see you—to hold you, to love you, to raise you in a perfect world. Think of how neat it will be to grow up in a place with no pain, sickness, or death. You will never have to experience hurt or be tempted by evil. I will never have to worry about friends influencing you the wrong way or about someone hurting you. You will grow up being able to talk to Jesus face-to-face. You are privileged, little one, not to have known the sufferings of this world!

My arms now ache to hold you, but I know that soon they will be filled. I love you and pray that Jesus will come quickly so we won't have to be separated very long. Until that day, rest well, little one, as you sleep in Jesus.

I love you.

Mommy

This mother defied society's tradition of silence concerning miscarriage by sending a "funeral announcement" to her friends and loved ones. In it she included two Bible texts—Psalm 139:16 and 1 Thessalonians 4:16 and 17—that gave her special comfort that she would hold her baby someday. Next to the texts she wrote, "Our little one brought joy into our lives for a few short weeks. Now we cling to the promise that we shall see our little one again and have the joy of raising our child in a perfect world. Thank you for your support and encouragement in our time of need." On the front of the announcement the couple wrote the name of their baby, the dates of conception and death, and a poem with an acrostics of the baby's name, Destiny Joy:

> Draw me closer, O my Lord.
> Embrace me in Your arms of love.
> Sustain me when my strength is gone.
> Transform my tears into a song.
> Increase my faith and comfort be
> Nearer, Lord. I do believe
> Your coming is not far away.
>
> Joy awaits me on that day.
> O God, my Destiny I see!
> You're holding her—like You held me!

On the back of the announcement are printed the following words: *Heaven is our Destiny. The peace of Jesus is our Joy.* As I finished reading the card, my eyes misted over with tears. I could understand their pain. I marveled at their courage in dealing with their loss.

Although each of these mothers had a different way of coping with the death of her child, all of them took the same basic steps of expressing their grief, recognizing its impact on their lives, and turning their pain into a tangible memorial to their miscarried child. Moving through each of these steps helped them cope with their sorrow in a positive way.

~ ~ ~

Acceptance did not come easily for me. Working toward it was often discouraging, but the effort was time well spent. Sometimes, though, when I felt anger surge through me or depression struck my newly found confidence, I feared I might be starting the process all over again. I could relate well to the words that C. S. Lewis wrote concerning the death of his wife:

"Grief is like a long and winding valley where any bend may reveal a totally new landscape. . . . Sometimes the surprise is the opposite one; you are presented with exactly the same sort of country you thought you left behind miles ago. That is when you wonder whether the valley isn't a circular trench. But it isn't. There are partial recurrences but the sequence doesn't repeat."[18]

Sometimes I too felt as though I was repeating my journey, but even though relapses occurred, I knew I was growing stronger. As I shared my feelings of grief over losing my baby, I was amazed at how people would then feel comfortable enough to talk to me about the pain in their lives. The words in 2 Corinthians 1:3, 4 suddenly came alive: "The Father of mercies and God of all comfort, who comforts us in all our tribulation, that we may be able to comfort those who are in any trouble, with the comfort with which we ourselves are comforted by God" (NKJV). Since discovering that comfort in God amid the tragedy of losing a child, I was able to encourage others. I could also understand what Judith Haimes said after she had suffered a loss. "If parents have some set goal, if they can help someone else, if they can become involved, they can survive. For the survivors, the key is to put other people ahead of themselves."[19]

As I reached out to others in pain, peace slowly grew inside me. No longer was I a lone soldier on a battlefield. Instead, I was simply one of many who had been wounded. Before the miscarriage, I had never experienced the tragedy of death. I could not relate well to the pain others had experienced. How casually I had acted when my next-door neighbor had miscarried! I figured it wasn't that big a deal, and never considered sending her a card or flowers. Even though we were close friends, I avoided talking about her miscarriage and left her to suffer through it alone, silently. It wasn't that I didn't really value her friendship; I just couldn't understand her grief.

Now I knew what it was like to lose a baby. This realization helped me to understand the suffering of others better. When my grandfather died, leaving my grandmother alone, I could relate to her pain of separation, and instinctively we grew closer. A friend who had been in a car accident lost not only her baby, but the use of her legs, confining her to a wheelchair. Her husband divorced her soon after, blaming her for their child's death. I couldn't even begin to comprehend such a calamity, but I understood better than I would have before my miscarriage.

Realizing that the world is full of hurting people helped me see my own loss in a different perspective. Even though I would never have dreamed that my loss could have any positive effects on my life, I was beginning to see some good results. I took time to read and write more. I had done a lot of research into miscarriages, typing phrases into my computer so I wouldn't forget certain facts.

Perhaps I could share some of my findings with other mothers who had experienced a similar loss. The idea excited me. Maybe my baby could make an impact on this world, even though he/she did not live to see it.

"If one is willing and courageous enough to experience life, the death of his child becomes a contribution, and life can be lived as a tribute to that child, as if that child's life had made a difference."[20]

I wanted to ensure that the short life of my baby would benefit the world somehow, even if it was in a small way. "Please, Lord," I prayed, "for my baby's sake and my own peace of mind, help me give You my hurt and let You make something beautiful out of it."

---

[1] L. Rich, *When Pregnancy Isn't Perfect,* p. 163.

[2] D. Hales and T. Johnson, *Intensive Caring,* p. 242.

[3] *Ibid.*

[4] M. Rank, *Free to Grieve,* p. 18.

[5] *Ibid.,* p. 28.

[6] *Ibid.,* p. 29.

[7] F. Toder, *When Your Child Is Gone,* p. 153.

[8] *Ibid.,* pp. 104-106.

[9] *Ibid.,* p. 27.

[10] Joan Bordow, *The Ultimate Loss: Coping With the Death of a Child* (New York: Beaufort Books, Inc., 1982), p. 19.

[11] Toder, p. 73.

[12] Rank, p. 42.

[13] *Ibid.*

[14] *Ibid.,* p. 41.

[15] Toder, p. 122.

[16] P. Vredevelt, *Empty Arms,* p. 22.

[17] Rank, p. 51.

[18] Vredevelt, p. 22.

[19] Katherine Fair Donnelly, *Recovering From the Loss of a Child* (New York: Macmillan Publishing Co., 1982), p. 131.

[20] Bordow, p. 66.

Chapter 8

SURVIVING THE PAIN

*The Lord has sent me to comfort those who mourn. . . . He sent me
to give them flowers in place of their sorrow, olive oil in place of tears,
and joyous praise in place of broken hearts. Isa. 61:2, 3, CEV.*

During the time of my healing I attended a seminar by Arlene Taylor, a brain-function consultant and risk manager at St. Helena Hospital in California. She explained the concept of grief recovery by using the analogy of a pyramid, showing three stages for working through the grieving process. Learning about these stages and coping strategies enabled me to find more effective ways of dealing with my pain.

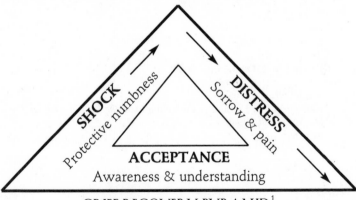

GRIEF RECOVERY PYRAMID[1]

GRIEF RECOVERY PYRAMID
Stage I—SHOCK
Symptoms may last from a few days to several weeks
Stage II—DISTRESS
Symptoms may last from a few weeks to two years
Stage III—ACCEPTANCE
Time lines will vary for each person

Shock. Shock, the "protective numbness" that occurs immediately after a tragedy, may last from a few days to several weeks. The following chart lists symptoms and suggested countermeasures for this stage.

STAGE I—SHOCK[2]	
Symptoms	*Recovery Strategies*
Agitation, confusion	Feel and show grief
Collapse, crying	Do not make major decisions
Denial or disbelief	Allow others to help you
Euphoria or hysteria	Rest and survive
Insomnia	Avoid substance abuse
Lethargy or weakness	Talk it out
Loss of appetite, nausea	Spend time in nature
Numbness or unreality	Spend time around *living* things

Distress. The second stage is distress. The sorrow and pain experienced in the distress stage may last from several weeks to as long as two years. I immediately identified myself in this stage, since the numbness of the initial shock of my miscarriage was nearly gone. Even though most of my family and friends expected me to be through this second stage as well, in reality I was still experiencing many of these distress symptoms.

STAGE II—DISTRESS[3]	
Symptoms	*Recovery Strategies*
Anger, anguish anxiety	Beware of rebounding
Crying, confusion	Acknowledge and verbalize
Fear, guilt, mood swings	emotional pain
Hopelessness; life seems	Keep decision-making to
to be in limbo	a minimum
Insomnia, restlessness	Allow yourself to mourn;
Low self-esteem	try journaling
Irrational decision-making	Accept the support/
Loneliness, isolation	assistance of others
Pain, physical illness	Check decisions with others
Poor judgment	Return to career or
Overeating, undereating,	volunteer work
improper diet	Get a physical examination
Slowed thinking	Heal at your own pace
Suicidal thoughts	Plan for good nutrition
	Get plenty of rest and exercise
	Seek and accept counseling

Acceptance. The length of time spent in the stages of awareness and understanding depends on the individual. However, it can and must be achieved if one is to heal emotionally. One can monitor his or her emotional growth by being aware of the symptoms and the countermeasures.

Although each stage of the grief recovery pyramid has unique symptoms and countermeasures, many overlap. Patience with oneself is vital, since recovery is a process, a journey. However, one may be able to speed

STAGE III—ACCEPTANCE[4]	
Symptoms	*Recovery Strategies*
Distress becomes	Cut final ties to loss and grief
less acute	Exercise consistently
Feel stronger and	Let go of *might-have-beens*
more energetic	Pamper yourself regularly
Interests return	Forgive yourself and others
Comfortable with self	Socialize; include new people
Have only periodic	Take control of your own life
crashes	Develop new interests
Loneliness surfaces	Learn to *act* rather
intermittently	than *react*
Physical symptoms decrease	
Nostalgia replaces emotional pain	
Return to optimum functioning	

recovery by pursuing the countermeasures and implementing coping techniques.

Taylor also shared insights on the impact grief has on the human brain. Fascinating research reveals that individuals tend to handle grief differently, determined by the parts of the brain and their functions.

Psychological Effects of Grief

First, one must understand something about the anatomy of the brain in order to comprehend its reaction to grief. The part of the brain that records past, present, and future events is the cerebrum (also called cortex, or gray matter). The cerebrum, the center for conscious thought and reasoning, sends and receives messages from the rest of the body, interprets them, and makes decisions about the information it has received. The cerebrum is divided by a natural fissure into the left and right hemispheres. In turn, each hemisphere is divided by another natural fissure, thereby defining four quadrants. Today brain researchers believe that most of us are born with a *brain lead*. The brain lead is an innate biochemical preference for processing information in one or two of these quadrants.

BRAIN LEAD AND EMOTIONS SUMMARY [5]	
Frontal Left *Prioritizing Mode*	*Frontal Right* *Visualizing Mode*

• Oblivious to emotion in self/ others and does not *read* nonverbal body language well (often due to a lack of access to the diagonal harmonizing mode)
• May be threatened by emotions, as they represent a potential for loss of *control*
• Expresses emotion through sarcasm, criticism, and *blowing up*
	• Perceives emotion in self, but may not *read* it very well in others
	• More comfortable with *change,* so less threatened by emotion
	• Expresses emotion through:
	  • Gesturing
	  • Tears/laughter
	  • Humor/prosody/drama/ stories

Basal Left *Organizing Mode*	*Basal Right* *Harmonizing Mode*

• Tries to avoid emotions, as they represent a potential for *change* from the status quo
• Not innately skilled at reading emotion in others
• May habitually maintain the emotion most often experienced
• Expresses emotion minimally
	• Very sensitive to emotion in self/others
	• Skilled at reading emotion/ nonverbals in others
	• Expresses emotion through:
	  • Affective speech/tonality
	  • Nonverbals (body position, smiles, frowns, touch)
	  • Drama/stories

Each of these parts—the frontal left, the basal left, the frontal right, and the basal right—has unique functions. The frontal left is the prioritizing part of the brain. It helps set one's goals, make decisions, manage willpower, and analyze information. The frontal left also understands and uses numbers, manages money and time, and utilizes audible speech to communicate.

If a person has a frontal left brain lead, they may become very frustrated when a miscarriage occurs, because the "goal" of having a healthy baby is not achieved. This frustration may cause the frontal left person to explode in anger at his/her helplessness. Immersing oneself in work in order to forget the pain is a common coping mechanism.

My husband definitely fit into this brain lead. Although he never expressed his anger by exploding, he buried himself in his work. At first I interpreted this as unthoughtful and uncaring behavior because I have a different brain lead. When I learned more about the brain, his grieving method suddenly made sense, and I no longer resented him for his reaction.

The basal left organizes information. This part of the brain loves routine. It allows a person to double think (perform a routine while thinking about something else). It is predictable, sequential, and contains memory banks for facts, figures, and labels. Also, it is the reading, writing, and spelling center. This node is very concrete and hates change. Since a miscarriage brings about an abrupt change, a person with this brain lead can suffer from intense stress and overexertion. Additionally, the basal left person may tend to mull over the details of the miscarriage and become frustrated with labels such as "spontaneous abortion," "habitual aborter," and "embryo" or "fetus" (instead of "baby"). Others may not understand the importance of these small details that the basal left person values. Since a miscarriage is not a "concrete death," according to society, a person with this brain lead often has trouble working through his/her grief, because this grief is not acknowledged by others.

The frontal right and basal right modes have equally important functions, although our sanity doesn't reward them to the extent it does the left-brain functions, especially in males. (Males are rewarded for frontal lobe functions, females for basal right functions.)

The frontal right mode of the brain has visualizing functions. It is spontaneous, imaginative, artistic, humorous, and willing to take a risk. A person with a frontal right brain lead often likes to solve problems, envisions change, and sees the big picture. Unfortunately, others may view this brain lead as unpredictable and unrealistic, as well as highly emotional, since a person with this lead tends to express emotions through tears. A miscarriage often leaves this type of person with questions *Why? Why? Why?* Anger may result from the inability to solve the problem of miscarriage, and its independent spirit may be interpreted by other brain leads as cold and uncaring.

The basal right mode, on the other hand, is a brain lead known for its sensitivity and harmonizing functions. A person with this preference is sentimental, relational, and musical. In this section the memory of emotions and feelings are stored, and information is collected through the sense of touch. Amazingly, researchers have recently discovered specific cells in this area of the brain that enable us to give meaning to spiritual experiences. Therefore, this part of the brain is often referred to as the center for spirituality.

A person with this brain lead may find comfort through hugs and nonverbal messages. With this mode it's not what you say, but how you say it, that's important. Because a person of this type is especially sensitive, he or she may become easily hurt by well-meaning but unthoughtful remarks such as "I'm sure you'll have another baby" or "It must have been God's will." Working through grief for the basal right may include making a scrapbook or a special wall hanging in memory of the miscarried child because of its great sentimental value. Close relationships are also important for sharing one's thoughts and feelings, both with God and with others. These types of activities hold great sentimental value. Harmony with God and others is a vital part of this mode. However, spiritual growth may come to a standstill if the person does not heal emotionally.

Of the four brain leads, I could relate to the basal right the best, especially after my miscarriage. I longed to crawl into Ken's arms and stay there. I needed to feel him touching me, assuring me that he was near. I was easily wounded by people who didn't understand my grief. Because of my strong need for deep relationships, I found that a spiritually oriented support group helped me work through my grieving process. I received great comfort in listening to Christian music. I remember going to a Christian bookstore not long after my miscarriage and buying a CD of praise songs. I played this music again and again. It seemed to boost my spirits and get me through another day.

My husband and I have opposite brain leads (which is common in marriage partners), so we dealt with the miscarriage very differently. There are no diagonal connectors in the brain. Since Ken's preference is the frontal left and mine is the basal right, we each must go through adjoining modes to get to the other's brain lead. This process takes effort, but can be done relatively easily if one chooses to do so. Not everyone is aware of this, however. (Perhaps this is one reason divorce and separation statistics rise following a miscarriage.)

Communication can be misunderstood because we also have a sensory preference (e.g., visual, auditory, kinesthetic) and use this sense in speaking. For example, one may say "I *feel* like nothing will ever be the same again." Another may respond "I don't *see* what you mean" or "You just *sound* depressed to me." Since 60 percent of the populace is estimated to be visual, and only 20 percent are auditory and 20 percent kinesthetic, husbands and wives may find communication trying if partners use different sensory systems and are unaware of this.[6]

Although personal preference, circumstances, and expectations can affect which part of the brain one uses, we can *choose* to use *any* of them. Just because a crisis can tend to suppress frontal function, a person is not bound to stay there. The choice can be made to overrule the brain's natural tendencies. A person's goal should be to develop and use all brain functions, always honoring one's brain lead in the process. Thirty minutes a day spent in stimulating brain exercise physically strengthens its ability to process information corporately. For example, a person can exercise their brain by doing something new every day. This simple task forces the brain out of its "comfort zone" and into new territory. God has given the human mind the ability of choice. A person can become a "whole-brain thinker" if they decide to make the effort.

The power of choice comes alive when the difference between emotions and feelings is understood. To begin with, emotions arise in the limbic system of the brain as a response to a stimulus. Physiological changes occur. One's hands may become sweaty and the knees may shake when one is put into a fearful environment. It takes six to seven seconds for the cerebrum to interpret the emotion and its physical changes in the body. "Feelings" is the label for this cerebral interpretation.

There are probably hundreds of feelings, but only a handful of core emotions, such as sadness, fear, anger, joy, and euphoria. These emotions are simply flashing lights that can be interpreted by the brain in a variety of ways. Therefore, a great amount of truth is found in the saying "If you want to change the way you feel, change the way you think." A person *can* control their feelings, since those feelings are the direct result of a decision made in the brain.

Even in the midst of grieving a miscarried child, a mother or father can choose a positive outlook. Listening to religious music, reading the Bible or other encouraging books, praying to the heavenly Father, or utilizing any other good techniques can help.

After learning about these amazing abilities of the brain, I better understood the correlation between grieving and the brain leads. Although I could not always control my emotions, I did have the power to manage my feelings. I could also change these feelings by dwelling on pleasant, uplifting thoughts. This knowledge encouraged me. God had not left me a helpless victim of circumstance when it came to my feelings. He provided a way out—and it's right inside my brain!

Differences Between the Grief of Men and Women

Men and women tend to exhibit different methods of coping with a loss, which explains the difficulties I had experienced in the past in understanding my husband's reaction to the miscarriage. According to Taylor's Grief

Recovery Outline, some of these differences may be innate to the male/female brain, while others are learned behaviors from environment and society.

The male brain is more "goal-oriented" and wants to "fix the problem" quickly. Because grief is a process, he may become frustrated at his helplessness and try to escape through work, activities, drugs, or even suicide. Since society often labels an emotional man as weak, he tends to hold his feelings inside and does not talk about his pain. However, he may "act it out" through violence or explosions of anger.

On the other hand, society encourages a female to express her emotions through crying or talking about her sorrow with other people. Nevertheless, a great danger exists of becoming caught in the trap of inaction. Since women are more "process-oriented," they can become stuck in the rehearsal of their grief and loss and continually brood over the incident, failing to move on toward acceptance and resolution.[7] A woman must learn to progress through the stages of grief, take constructive action, and allow herself to heal.

In light of the differences in how men and women grieve, many couples have problems in their marriage after a miscarriage. Instead of supporting each other, one partner is often hurt in their mate's response to the loss. Learning the different coping mechanisms of each sex can help a couple understand each other and build their relationship. If men can learn to express their grief verbally, they can not only relate better to their wives, but they can also gain emotional healing. Women likewise can learn from men how to take action instead of dwelling on their loss and letting it paralyze their productivity. Through working together, both men and women can learn to share their grief and take steps toward recovery.

GENDER GRIEVING STYLES SUMMARY[8]	
♀ FEMALES	♂ MALES
Stereotypically	*Stereotypically*
• Exhibit a process-oriented grieving style • Tend to want to articulate their loss and grief, to verbalize it to friends and family • Have often been socialized to be more comfortable expressing grief through tears • May overprocess and begin to brood • Endlessly rehearse the incident believing that *talking* about it is enough, even though taking some action could help them to cope more effectively	• Exhibit a goal-oriented grieving • Want to *fix* the predicament • Tend to *run away* (literally or figuratively) when they can't fix it • Avoid verbalizing grief (are silent) but may act it out in their behaviors • Allow unresolved grief to build up inside where it can explode later on when a similar (but unrelated) incident triggers the emotion of sadness
Need-to Challenges • Learn to take constructive *action* whether or not they feel like it at the moment • Avoid perpetually indulging negative feelings *and* brooding endlessly	*Need-to Challenges* • Learn to *articulate* grief and act out feelings in an appropriate manner • Realize that emotional pain won't truly resolve on its own

Tips for Grief Recovery

Taylor suggests several tips for couples to utilize during the grieving process. They include:

• **Give up denial.** Admit that a problem exists, that there has been a loss. Assert that you are now willing to deal with your grief. Give up blaming yourself and others.

• **Start to take action.** Instead of just thinking about recovery, begin to act.

- **Find a same-gender friend and join a support group.** It is more difficult to recover alone. Be totally honest about your episodes of loss, and require confidentiality of friends/support group.

- **Learn to journal.** Write a *loss history,* or create a graph of specified personal losses, noting the dates when they occurred, so you can clearly visualize them.

- **Move beyond the loss**—through awareness, through the utilization of a support system, and the inclusion of appropriate activities.

- **Develop a spiritual relationship with a Higher Power.** A friendship with God can help you to work through feelings of guilt and shame (including false guilt and shame), hopelessness, and depression.

Each of these tips will help both men and women to move successfully through the grief recovery process. Through encouragement, understanding, and help from God and a support group of friends, a couple can learn to work together so that they can gain emotional healing and grow stronger in their relationship with one another.

---

[1] © Arlene Taylor, Ph.D., Realizations, Inc./Success Resources International.

[2] *Ibid.*

[3] *Ibid.*

[4] *Ibid.*

[5] *Ibid.*

[6] Notes from Taylor's seminar.

[7] Information from a handout at Taylor's seminar.

[8] © Arlene Taylor, Ph.D., Realizations, Inc./Success Resources International.

Chapter 9

MY GOD OF PEACE
AND COMFORT

*I will heal you, lead you, and give you comfort, until those who are
mourning start singing my praises. No matter where you are, I,
the Lord, will heal you and give you peace. Isa. 57:18, 19, CEV.*

As time passed, my healing progressed. Family
and friends sent gifts, cards, and letters. One
church member brought me a beautiful silk
flower arrangement to hang on my wall.
Another sent me a baby gift, a book, and a little stuffed
lamb. I wondered how she had known that I was planning
the "Jesus' Little Lamb" theme in my nursery. This gift was
especially precious to me since it brought hope that I
would have another baby. Just knowing that someone else
thought I would conceive again was encouraging.

The most meaningful gift I received, however, was a
simple letter from a church member I barely knew. She
had experienced a miscarriage and was familiar with the
pain I was feeling. She wrote about her experience, shared
her honest feelings, and sent quotations and texts that had
brought her comfort. Her words held so much faith and
wisdom! The fact that a casual acquaintance would open

up to me in such a personal way touched me deeply. I was so grateful she had taken the time to share a delicate part of herself with me. Tears washed my eyes and soothed my heart as I read:

Dear Ken and Missy,

Just wanted to let you know how sorry we are that the baby died and to tell you that all of us are praying that the Lord will be with you in this time of sorrow.

Having had a miscarriage three years ago, we can understand some of what you are going through. Things are pretty devastating, because all your expectations, hopes, and dreams for that child are taken from you. Our experience showed us that we hurt and longed for that baby, even though we already had three children. The pain of losing our child, though unborn, hurt in many ways as much as losing our first son when he was a year old.

As hard as the experience was for me personally, I can say now that it brought me into a deeper relationship with God. I can say that I know that it is not God's will for me or you to lose our children, because God is a giver of life. However, what He allows to touch us He is able to help us cope with to where we can glorify Him.

God is not offended by my questions of why or my feelings of deep disappointment, anger, sadness, and depression. He invites me to bring all of this to Him, and while He did not make everything (or anything) clear to me at that time, I was still brought to a greater understanding of the character of God. I learned there are times my relationship with God may be called into question in the heavenly courts, and the Lord may be allowing me to go through a difficult experience because He knows my faith better than I do myself. He can see things beyond my scope of vision and knows what would be best for me. What I gained was a deeper level of trust in God and knowing that Jesus really did understand what I was going through.

I'm thankful for several things for you:

First, I'm glad that you have each other and a stable marriage. I encourage you to keep the lines of communication open. Because I was physically affected by the miscarriage, I'm sure my husband got tired of the way I would go over things. But he always listened, and that helped a lot (even now).

I'm glad that there is family close by. It was so nice to have my mother come out and simply take care of all of us. We needed a lot of tender loving care then.

I'm thankful that you know that a pregnancy can occur, and our hope is that you will be able to become pregnant again (soon), and that all will go well.

I'm thankful that you didn't have to spend much time in the hospital and didn't require any major surgeries or have any tumors removed.

Another thing to be thankful for is that you have good insurance. (We didn't have any three years ago.)

Many times people don't know what to say and don't say anything, or they say shallow things that sometimes hurt more than help. I wanted you to know that we care and, most of all, that we serve a living God who is able to understand and sustain us in times of trouble.

I am enclosing the words to a couple songs. It always helps me to focus on hymns and Scripture when I'm going through difficult times. "He Giveth More Grace" is a favorite that has helped me several times, and "He Is Faithful" is a new one that I am learning. I hope the words will bring a measure of comfort.

If you ever need to talk, I'm available for listening. Take care of yourselves.

Love, Rita

My fingers flipped to the next page, and my eyes found the lyrics. "He giveth more grace. . . ." "He's been faithful. . . ." I wanted to believe those words. My mind knew God is always faithful to His children, but my heart cried out for reassurance of His love.

I began searching through my Bible for words to get me through another day. I decided to make a list of Bible texts that were especially meaningful to me, and then summarize them in my own words.

Job 13:15	Though He slay me, yet will I trust Him.
Job 23:10	He knows the way, and, when tested, I will come forth as gold.
Ps. 57:1-3	He's with me in my calamities.
Ps. 34:19	The Lord delivers me from affliction.
Ps. 55:22	If I cast my burdens on Him, He will sustain me.
Ps. 40:4	He promises happiness if I trust the Lord.
Ps. 34:18	God is near brokenhearted, saves crushed in spirit.
Ps. 17:8	I am the apple of God's eye.
Ps. 147:3	He heals my broken heart and binds up my wounds.
Isa. 26:3	He keeps me in perfect peace.
Isa. 40:10	I need not fear; God strengthens and holds me.
Isa. 32:17	He gives righteousness, peace, and assurance.
Isa. 40:11	Jesus holds lambs in arms, leads those with young.
Matt. 11:28	He grants me rest when I am heavy laden.
John 14:27	He promises me peace.
John 10:10	Jesus gives me life more abundantly.
Rom. 15:13	My God of hope fills me with happiness.

I wondered what the future would bring. Would I ever get pregnant again? All my plans had done an about-face after the baby died. Where would I go from here? Once more I found myself pouring out my frustrations in my prayer journal.

Dear Father,

I know I've heard that "nothing lies beyond the reach of prayer except that which lies outside the will of God." But I guess I don't feel like believing those words. School ended today, and my heart was sad as I told my students goodbye. I won't be back next year. I feel lost. I'm not sure who I am anymore—not a mother, not a teacher. I guess that leaves "housewife," which can be lonely at times.

To add to my feelings of insecurity, I received two cards in the mail—a sympathy card from someone I can't even place, and a note from my pen pal. She's pregnant with a little girl and was due yesterday, Father's Day.

Maybe it was the combination of the two, I don't know, but I felt a sharp knife in my chest and an uncanny sense of being smothered.

Father, I need You. I need Your presence and Your peace. Please grip my hand tightly and never let it go. I can't trust You without Your help. Lord, I choose to give You my life today. Dear Jesus, please let me have another baby soon, if it is Thy will—a healthy baby boy or girl.

Missy

Chapter 10

A CHANGE OF EVENTS

Before I made you in your mother's womb, I chose you. Before you were born, I set you apart for a special work. Jer. 1:5, NCV.

Three long months of waiting passed after my miscarriage. As each period began, it reminded me of the hard, cold fact that I was not pregnant. Toward the end of the fourth month one of my best friends called me from the hospital. She had just given birth to her first child. Her excitement and joy reopened the fresh wounds of my soul. Numbly I floundered for something to say, desperately searching for words that would hide the pain. I wanted to be happy for her; I truly did. It was just that our babies were supposed to have been delivered a month apart. In fact, she had been there the day I had discovered I was pregnant. Now she had her child—a healthy baby boy.

And I had nothing. Nothing but the pain that threatened to engulf me at any moment. I struggled to keep my voice from cracking. At last the conversation ended, and as I hung up the receiver, my shoulders shook with uncontrollable sobs.

I just want my baby back! The words screamed again and again in my mind. How could it hurt this much when I thought I was healing? Where was the peace I had so recently found? I cried until no more tears would come. I wrote in my prayer journal:

It seems that everyone can have a baby except me. I'm due to start my period today or tomorrow. Already I'm sure I'll start, because my temperature dropped and I feel as though I'm beginning to cramp. Maybe it was too much to hope for, getting pregnant the first month we started trying again, but then, why not? I'm trying to trust You. I really am. I'm supposed to "wait on the Lord's help" [see Ps. 27:14] and "praise God because He has heard my prayer for help. He is my strength and shield; I trust Him, and He helps me. He will be my shepherd and carry me forever" [see Ps. 28:6-9]. Oh, Lord, please help me put my trust in You and quit feeling sorry for myself! I guess I just need to be carried awhile.

Even though I was certain my period would start, day after day passed. My temperature had gone back up, and I had never started cramping, though I did find a small trace of blood when I went to the bathroom. This discovery only made me more certain I wasn't pregnant.

The suspense was too much to bear. I picked up a home pregnancy test at the grocery store, planning to take it when Ken got home. Six months had passed since I had taken my last test. Could I possibly be pregnant again? I didn't dare hope; the disappointment would be too great.

That night my hands trembled as I waited for the test results. This time I did not close my eyes but kept them fixed on the stick, my heart racing, more from fear than excitement. *Two lines—positive!* I couldn't believe it. Part of me wanted to scream and dance for joy, and part of me was terrified at the possibility of having another miscarriage. I stumbled to the garage.

"Well, what did it say?" Ken asked.

"I'm pregnant."

"Really?" he replied, as surprised as I was. He took me into his arms and asked, "How do you feel?"

I was still shaking. "I'm scared."

He held me tighter and suggested that we have special prayer, right there, for our new baby. So we did.

This time we didn't tell anyone. I had prayed for a baby for my birthday present. This one was due the last week of March, near my birthday.

As the days passed everything worried me, especially the fact that I wasn't sick enough. This wasn't a good sign! My mother had been very sick with both my brother and me. The absence of nausea constantly reminded me of the termination of my previous pregnancy. The doctor said I had to wait until eight weeks for a sonogram, about the time my first baby had died.

I prayed constantly. Somehow I knew God wouldn't let me go through another miscarriage; it would be too much to bear. I couldn't handle it, and I told Him so. I longed for reassurance that everything was OK. "What ifs" continually filled my mind. I was haunted by the thought that the same nightmare might recur. I found myself writing down my joys and concerns in my prayer journal.

Dear Father,

I'm officially four weeks pregnant. Ken and I had decided not to tell anyone, but my mother asked the day after I found out, so I couldn't help telling her. Only a few people know.

I go in for my first doctor's appointment next Thursday. My doctor may take a sonogram to be sure that the baby is in my uterus and not in my tube. If so, the heart should be beating, and I will be able to see it on the sonogram. I'm almost afraid to go in for my checkup. What if there is no heartbeat? I fear that I will always worry about this. I haven't been sick, really. My breasts have been a bit sore, but I just don't have very many signs. I wish I were sicker, so I'd know I was pregnant. I'm so scared it will all go away!

Oh, Lord, I praise You for making me pregnant again. I am so thankful! I claim the promises of Your protection and guidance. Please help me trust in You and believe that You hold my baby and me in Your arms. I love You, Father, and I love my baby. Help me keep my love in that order.

Missy

This prayer of surrender would help me survive the next few weeks. Although I desperately wanted a baby, I realized that God must be in partnership with my desire. Perhaps the timing was not right. Or maybe God had a different plan altogether for my life. I didn't know. But God did. He was in control, and He knew what lay ahead.

Chapter 11

REPLAY

God will bless you, if you don't give up when your faith is being tested. He will reward you with a glorious life, just as he rewards everyone who loves him. James 1:12, CEV.

The day came for my prenatal checkup. As I walked into the doctor's office, fear and dread swept over me as I looked at the familiar surroundings. My mind flashed back to the painful memories hiding within these walls. Four months had passed, yet it seemed like just yesterday when our hope for a healthy baby had been ripped from our hearts.

Following a nurse into an examination room, I watched as if in a dream as the technician hooked me to the sonogram machine. A picture suddenly appeared. I could see the pregnancy ring (this time I knew what to look for), but why was there nothing in it? If the baby were as old as the last one had been when it had died, I knew I should be seeing a head and a body. But there was nothing—no flashing, no heartbeat. The nightmare was back.

The doctor insisted everything looked normal—for a 4-week-old baby, not an 8-week-old. If I had been in the last week of my cycle at conception, he said, then it was possible that the baby was fine, just very young. We would know for sure in another week. By then the baby would have to have a heartbeat.

Ken and I left the clinic, terribly hurt and disappointed. Not knowing was almost worse than if we were certain the baby was dead. The main reason I had gone in for the sonogram was to get reassurance. Now more worry flooded my mind. How would I ever make it a whole week? The rest of the day was a blur.

When I awoke the next morning, the memory of the day before jolted me to reality in a flash. Ken had already left for work, and loneliness washed over me. I had no one to confide in, to pray for me, to encourage me. I was totally alone.

"Where are You, God? Why aren't You answering when I talk to You? Have You left me too?" I buried my head in my pillow and sobbed. Time seemed to stand still. When I could cry no longer, depression hit. Angrily I tried to go about my daily routine.

Finally I gave up. Nothing mattered anymore. I could think of nothing else. "Oh, God, this can't be happening again! You can't do this to me! I can't trust You, Lord. What if You let this baby die?"

The probability of another miscarriage was almost certain. I knew God could work a miracle. I still believed He could intercede. But what if He didn't? What if He allowed my second child to die just as He had the first? Could I still follow Him? Could I still believe that He loved me and had my best interests in mind?

I had to choose. Either I denounced the Lord and the control He had in my life, or I surrendered all to His will, whatever the cost—even if it meant losing another baby. It was the hardest decision I had ever had to make. The terrible struggle nearly pulled me in two. I now knew personally what it was like to wrestle with God. I was exhausted, physically and mentally. At last I could stand it no longer. It was worse fighting against the Lord than surrendering to His plan for my life.

"All right, Father, You can have my life. It's a mess. I don't want it. I'd rather die. I don't want to be in control, because I don't have the power to change anything anyway. Whatever You want, Lord. I don't understand, but I choose to follow You. Please, just help me get through this week!"

Silence.

But it was a different silence. Not angry, accusing, bitter. Almost a peace. It was over. God had won. So why was I feeling better? I didn't know, and I didn't really care. At least the pain in my heart was bearable. Relief swept over me. I felt as though a ton of bricks had been lifted from my shoulders.

Several times during the next few days I longed for human companionship and encouragement. The only one I told about my situation was the neighbor across the street. I asked if her church might pray for me. I felt as though I needed prayers. Several times I picked up the phone to call someone from my church, but what would I say? Since we had decided to keep this pregnancy a secret, I didn't feel I could ask anyone for prayer without explaining all the details. I didn't want everyone at church to know. Not again. Ken tried to be there for me, but I longed for womanly companionship.

Then it was Thursday. Ken didn't eat breakfast. He was fasting, he said. He wasn't praying that the baby would be all right, just that God's will would be done.

My mother met us at the waiting room. I almost wished she hadn't come. The first miscarriage had been so hard on her that I wished to spare her any further pain.

Nevertheless, I was grateful for her concern and support.

The nurse led us into the examining room. Once again the familiar picture appeared on the screen. There was the pregnancy ring in my uterus—but no flashing. I wasn't surprised. Somehow God had cushioned the shock. Tears trickled down my cheeks, but this time I held back the sobs. Ken's hand tightened on my shoulder. He knew.

The doctor confirmed what we already knew. The baby had not grown. There was no heartbeat. She called it a "blighted ovum." Not even a fetus. She was sorry.

"I'm going home," I told her firmly. "I'll have the miscarriage there."

She was not pleased with my decision, but she couldn't change my mind. I was still paying the bills from the last miscarriage and couldn't afford the expense of another surgery. Days of waiting lay ahead. When would it occur? I hoped I wouldn't be alone. Would it be terribly painful?

Nearly two weeks passed. I felt cramping intermittently and was sure it would happen any day. My emotions were all out of whack. I seemed to have no energy to do anything. Out of pure determination, I sent out my résumés for a substitute teaching job in the Christian and Catholic school systems. I had quit my night job because the timing interfered with my substituting. Now I wondered if I had made a mistake. What if I didn't get called to work? My life seemed to be spinning out of control.

Again and again I gave my concerns to God, yet I could feel myself beginning to worry again. So many questions tumbled around in my mind. What if we couldn't pay our bills? What if the miscarriage occurred at the wrong time or place? What if I had to go in for an emergency D & C? What if the doctors were wrong, and I was still pregnant?

Long days alone dragged by. I tried to preoccupy myself with housework, but I began sinking deeper into despair. Ken could do nothing but wait for the miscarriage with me. His helplessness frustrated both of us, yet his presence enabled me to survive. We had just celebrated our seventh wedding anniversary, and I was grateful for such a strong marriage. Although he could not fully understand my pain, he was still there for me. I held on to him tightly, and he continued to be my strength and companion.

But only God could give the comfort my heart cried for, and only by letting go could I receive His power. He seemed to be reminding me that where there is no control, there is no responsibility. I could do nothing about the miscarriage. I had absolutely no control over when, where, or how it would happen. Therefore, God did not hold me responsible. I had to trust Him—trust His timing and His way.

Please, God, take hold of my hand. Get me through this awful time. I need Your strength, Your power. I have none of my own. I claim Your promise that You will not forsake me. Help me to believe Your Word. Just get me through this day, this hour, this moment.

I decided that perhaps I could fight my depression by placing Bible texts around the house, a good idea I discovered from Barbara Johnson's book *Splashes of Joy in the Cesspools of Life.* I hung a Bible verse in every room, over each electrical switch, and then put a few more on my bathroom mirrors and walls. No matter which room I was in, a verse hung somewhere close. If I felt despair returning, I would immediately find the text and repeat its message in my mind. In this way I was able to memorize scriptures easily and quickly. When friends noticed the verses and asked what purpose they served, I had the perfect opportunity to share my source of strength with them. Through these conversations I developed closer relationships, thus fulfilling my own need of friendship.

It was these verses of encouragement that helped me survive the days that followed. I read Psalm 23:4 again and again as I waited for the waves of pain to begin: "Even though I walk through the valley of the shadow of death, I will fear no evil, for you are with me" (NIV). Somehow God used these words to draw near to me in the midst of my crisis.

One day when I was feeling especially depressed, I flipped the button on my stereo and discovered a Christian station I had never been able to pick up before—the broadcasting area had just been extended. When I needed it most, words of comfort poured into my house through the messages of songs. I considered this gift a special blessing, sent directly from God to remind me of His closeness.

God had not forsaken me, yet I couldn't understand why He was allowing me to suffer through a second miscarriage. My emotions seesawed up and down. Sometimes I caught glimpses of God's care for me, but at other times I could see only my empty arms and feel the pain inside.

The first week in September I began having light contractions. My due date for my first baby had been September 2, but instead of giving birth, I was experiencing a second miscarriage.

The cramping worsened, but nothing happened. I had once been afraid of the sight of blood; now I longed for it, prayed for it. Saturday passed, then Sunday. Monday brought more cramping; Tuesday, more pain. By Wednesday I was hurting so badly I could do nothing but lie in bed. The contractions came regularly, but still not accompanied by much bleeding.

Worse than the physical pain was the mental anguish. I felt worthless as a wife. Anyone could have children, but look at me! I had messed it up twice in a row. What was wrong with me, anyway? My whole life seemed to be sinking into a black abyss, and I had no power to do anything about it. The waiting was driving me crazy. Ken could go on living a normal life of work, hobbies, and fun while I did nothing but live and breathe miscarriage. It was so easy to feel sorry for myself.

By Thursday morning I determined that *nothing* was going to keep me in bed another day. I didn't care if I were in pain; I decided to clean my house. Oh, I might be totally losing control of my body and my life, but not of my house—that I could control. With the aid of several aspirin I was able to get quite a bit done, and having even a small amount of order in my life helped. But nothing could have prepared me for what lay ahead.

Around 1:00 Friday morning I was awakened by a sharp contraction that nearly took my breath away. I managed to stumble to the bathroom. It was coming. I hadn't even gotten over the first contraction before another one hit. Fear swept over me as a third contraction rose. *I never thought it would hurt this bad!* I seemed to be in an ocean of pain as wave after wave rolled over me.

Minutes ticked by. Contraction. Rest. Contraction. Breathe.

At 2:00 I woke Ken. He seemed both relieved and worried when he realized what was happening. As he rubbed my back, the contractions continued. I squeezed his arm as the pain swept over me. Would it ever end?

Around 4:00 the pain worsened. One great contraction rolled over me, but instead of passing, it remained. I could find no relief. I began pushing and felt something literally being ripped away, as though part of my body was tearing apart.

The pain never returned. The nightmare was finished.

Strangely, I felt like a new person. The depression I had carried for weeks vanished. I was glad it was over. I determined never again to have a natural miscarriage. The mental anguish had been more devastating than the physical pain.

Now that my hormones were beginning to stabilize, I gained new determination to go on with my life. But the future seemed as dark and vast as a moonless midnight sky. Would I ever have a healthy baby?

Chapter 12

FINDING SUPPORT

Praise God, the Father of our Lord Jesus Christ! The Father is a merciful God, who always gives us comfort. He comforts us when we are in trouble, so that we can share the same comfort with others in trouble. We share in the terrible sufferings of Christ, but also in the wonderful comfort he gives. 2 Cor. 1:35, CEV.

Although many church members had tried to be supportive through my first miscarriage, I felt alone and cut off from my church family during my second one. I almost resented the fact that no one knew what I was going through, even though it was my own fault for not having had the courage to tell anyone.

Why had I not made closer friends? Two years should have been plenty of time. Often I had longed for a small prayer group in which I could get to know some of the women in my church more personally. But no such group existed.

One day as I was having my morning devotions, feeling especially lonely and sorry for myself, I came across a text in Psalms that left a strong impression on me. When paraphrased in my own words, it said that God had heard my prayer and answered it, but I must be willing to do my part.

"OK, God," I responded, "so what exactly is my part?"

Loud and clear, a voice seemed to reply, "Start your own prayer group."

Shocked at the directness of the answer, I stopped reading. Maybe that was it. Maybe God was calling me to *do* something about my grief, not just hide it away inside of myself. My mind shot back to the conversations I'd had with so many hurting people. Surely other women like me would be willing to share their experiences of how God had helped them get through their pain. It seemed so simple that I marveled at myself for not thinking of it earlier. Yes, perhaps this was my ministry—to comfort hurting people. The more I thought about the idea, the more excited I became.

But I met all kinds of obstacles when I shared my idea. One would think the pastoral staff would welcome the suggestion of starting a women's prayer group, but this was not the case. There were already too many programs . . . Perhaps it would cut into the attendance at prayer meeting . . . Scheduling was impossible . . . Probably no one would be interested in it anyway.

I hung up the phone in tears. Why had I thought God had given me such an idea? I was shocked at the coldness of the response I'd received and almost decided to abandon the thought completely.

Then at church the next week a guest speaker encouraged the forming of small groups. He said it was vital for developing a close church family. I felt as though God Himself were speaking to me, encouraging me to continue plans for a women's prayer group.

After church the following week I decided to do my own polling to see if there might be enough interest. Maybe once a week was too often. How about once a month? Then no one could say it interfered with the weekly programs. The schedule would be flexible—we could choose whichever day was convenient. Perhaps I could tell my testimony about how I needed support when I was going through my miscarriages and hadn't felt close enough to call anyone in the church. I would be very vulnerable. Would I break down and cry? The thought scared me. What if no one really cared?

Immediately I pulled out a church directory and began making a list of the names of women who were close to my age. I decided I would call each of them and invite them to a supper, followed by a Bible study and prayer time. This small group setting would allow me to get to know the women in my church personally, and perhaps after we got acquainted we could strengthen each other.

My fingers shook as I dialed the first number. But to my delight she accepted the invitation, and so did several others.

The night of the meeting I could barely contain my excitement—or my fear. What if no one liked the idea of starting a women's group each month? It seemed that I had so much resting on this idea that it just *had* to work! I reminded myself of the conviction I had felt only a week earlier, and somehow I knew God would not forsake me. If a prayer group was His will, why should I worry? If not, then He would provide some other means of support.

My voice trembled as I welcomed eight young women into my home. There had been more who had said they would come, but I was still pleased with the turnout. I didn't want a large group; it would be easier to be more open with a few. Sandwiches and munchies were served, and everyone seemed to be enjoying their conversations.

All too soon the last bites were eaten, and it was time for me to begin the meeting. Each woman had been asked to complete a list of her favorite things. I read each list, then everyone tried to guess who the person was. I learned many interesting facts from this simple exercise. After the last person had been introduced, it was time for my testimony and the reason I had invited everyone to my home.

Drawing a deep breath, I explained how lonely I had been since my second miscarriage. I hadn't told anyone, I said, because I just couldn't pick up the phone and say, "Hi, I'm having a miscarriage." I shared with them the longing I felt for a women's group that would meet regularly for Bible study and prayer. I believed this kind of fellowship would be an encouragement for those who were struggling through painful times.

As my story unfolded, I noticed several women had tears in their eyes. As others shared their testimony, we discovered that pain was a common thread to which everyone could relate. One woman was going through a divorce. Another had problems with her family. A third desperately wanted to find a mate, but even after praying for several years, she had found no one. Others were going through difficult marriages and financial struggles.

I definitely was not alone! Although not all shared in my pain over the death of a child, every woman could relate with the sorrow of losing someone or something that was important in her life.

After the testimonies had ended, I shared some meaningful Bible scriptures that had helped me through my grief, and others, in turn, offered theirs. Then we made a prayer list and decided to send baked goods and a note to one of the names, saying we were praying for that person. Toward the close, the vote was unanimous to continue meeting regularly, and a friend of mine offered to have it at her house the following month. Even after we formally dismissed the group, several women lingered, giving each other hugs and encouraging words before slipping away.

Watching the last car disappear, I felt the warmth of the evening fill my soul. "Thank You, Lord. You do care! You knew this was just what I needed. You certainly have answered my prayer—with many more friendships than I'd ever dreamed possible!"

Chapter 13

COPING WITH WORRY

Don't worry about anything, but pray about everything.
With thankful hearts offer up your prayers and requests to God.
Then, because you belong to Christ Jesus, God will bless you
with peace that no one can completely understand. And this
peace will control the way you think and feel. Phil. 4:6, 7, CEV.

Three months passed before we could even attempt pregnancy again. During this time I struggled to help make ends meet by substitute teaching and by writing for magazines. Every morning I would wait by the phone to see if I would get called to work. More often than not, the phone wouldn't ring, and I'd find myself in front of my computer. I sent several poems and a short story I had written in college to several magazines. As the days passed I received letter after letter of rejection.

The doctor bills mounted, and so did my desperation. How would we ever afford all the expense? We hadn't paid all the hospital bills from my first miscarriage, and there were bills for sonograms, office visits, and medications connected with my second miscarriage. There simply wasn't enough money!

I had given up my job to stay home with my baby. Now I had no job and no baby—but lots of bills. "O Lord," I pleaded, "just let us break even this month. I don't know how we can do this, but with You, Lord, all things are possible."

Month after month passed, and the Lord provided. Somehow the bills got paid, one at a time. Even through finances the Lord seemed to be reminding me that He was in control. Nothing was too hard for Him, if only I would trust.

However, trusting was easier on some days than on others. When I was able to secure a job in the adult education program, I praised God for His blessings. But rejection letters and unexpected expenses often tested my faith, and I would wonder if God really knew what He was doing.

I had always been so busy, never stopping a moment to sit down and reflect. Now I had plenty of time to do both. What was God's will for my life? I had always assumed I would teach for a few years until I got pregnant, then I'd stay home and raise my children—and maybe write part-time. Suddenly my plans were drastically changed. No longer was I an elementary teacher or a mother. The children in my life had somehow vanished. Even my writing continued to be rejected, and I began to wonder if I were worth anything to anybody.

I decided to start an exercise program. Maybe that would lift my depression. Even though I had never enjoyed working out, I vowed, out of pure determination, to do an aerobics tape three times a week. Gradually I began noticing results. Other people took note of the pounds I was losing, including my husband. With his strong encouragement I kept up the routine, knowing that I not only felt better, but that the benefits of regular exercise were helping me overcome my feelings of low self-worth. And I would be in better shape when (and if) I got pregnant again.

The self-discipline that resulted from exercising carried over into my spiritual life. The aerobic tapes I used contained uplifting religious music. After exercising I found it easier to sit down in my overstuffed chair with my Bible and study God's Word. These quiet times helped me regroup my thoughts, plan my activities, and most important, ask God what He had in store for me for the day. Through prayer and journaling I found a closeness with God I hadn't had time to develop before.

September rolled by, and the first week of October arrived. Eagerly I made arrangements to attend a women's spiritual retreat in Nebraska with my mother and grandmother. Arriving at the hotel where the meetings were to be held, we received our schedules for the weekend and a list of speakers and workshops. I was amazed to discover the main speaker would be giving tips on how to overcome guilt, depression, and worry—my top three battles.

Even more surprising, the speaker that night read a letter from a mother who had lost her baby in a miscarriage. In the note the mother shared her intense pain and how her grief threatened her relationship with God. Tears rolled down my cheeks as I listened to her testimony, so similar to my own. I knew the sting of death and the confusion it could cause spiritually. I couldn't get over the perfect timing of her message for me.

We must learn to release our worry that causes depression (Prov. 12:25), the presenter explained. Only by consciously choosing can Christians give their anguish to God and experience His peace. In His Word God gives specific instruction for fighting anxiety. By following these practical steps, one can overcome worry:

1. *Determine whether your worry is over a real need, or a de-*

sire/want. If it's a desire/want, realize you may never get it (Phil. 4:11). If it's a real need, trust God to supply that need (Phil. 4:19).

2. *Pray about your specific worry and your tendency to worry.* Talk to God as you would talk to a friend. Tell Him all your concerns. Ask Him to supply your need according to His will—in His timing. Ask for the peace He promises in Philippians 4:6, 7.

3. *Read your Bible daily—even when you don't "feel" like it.* God's Word will give you peace and strength to carry on, but you must open it and search.

4. *Memorize Bible texts and promises that speak to your specific worry.* When you begin to worry, repeat them out loud.

5. *Make "trust" cards.* On one side of a 3 x 5 card write TRUST in bold letters. On the reverse side write a Bible text or promise that speaks to your specific worry. Place these cards around the house, in your purse, etc. When you begin to worry, take a card and read "TRUST." Then turn it over and read God's promise to you.

6. *Dwell on good things in place of worry.* With God's help you can control what you choose to dwell on—thoughts full of worry or thoughts of trust.

7. *Practice rejoicing instead of worrying.* When you begin to worry, sing a song, pray a prayer of thanksgiving, recall all the good things God has done for you, or read Bible verses that speak of praise (Ps. 34:1; 118:24; Phil. 4:4-8; 1 Thess. 5:16-18).

8. *Trust that God has a perfect plan for your life.* He is in control. If you're His child, nothing can happen unless He, in His love and wisdom, permits it (Prov. 30:5).

9. *Seek God and His kingdom first—not your own concerns.* He'll take care of everything else (Matt. 6:33).*

Never before had I received such practical advice on

how to overcome my worry! I was certainly a prime victim for anxiety: I was concerned about finances, my inability to have children, and my own worth as a person. It was such a relief to find spiritual knowledge for fighting my worry. Perhaps if I applied these suggestions I could leave my concerns in God's hands, where they belonged.

---

* God-controlled Emotions Seminar, by Nancy Canwell, associate pastor, Walla Walla College church.

Chapter 14

CONFLICT

*The righteous cry out, and the Lord hears them; he delivers them
from all their troubles. The Lord is close to the brokenhearted
and saves those who are crushed in spirit. Ps. 34:17, 18, NIV.*

Not long after the women's retreat, Ken's brother
called to tell us his wife was going to have a ce-
sarean section the following weekend. He
wanted all the family to be present for the birth
of his baby girl. I had known they were expecting, but had
tried to push the thought out of my mind. She had become
pregnant a month after I first had. The pain and injustice
swept over me once more as I listened to the plans for the
family celebration.

Finally I could stand it no longer. Hanging up the
phone, I threw myself on my bed and sobbed. I was supposed to be happy for them, but all I could think about
was that I should be holding a baby in my empty arms. My
heart's wound was too fresh. Just seeing a newborn still re-
duced me to tears. I knew I could never make it through a
whole weekend.

I determined not to go. I would not subject myself to
such torture. Part of me was angry that Ken's brother had
even called. Couldn't they understand? They had heard

about my miscarriages. Why had they dared to make such a thoughtless request? Deep inside I knew they were inviting us to share in their joy and meant no harm. In fact, they had experienced miscarriages in the past, and they had had one premature baby boy, now nearly 2.

Later Ken asked me what I wanted to do about the invitation. Since we had such short notice, he would have to let them know our plans immediately. "You know how much this means to my family—my folks and brothers will all be there. I really think we should go."

I stared at him in disbelief; certain I had not heard him correctly. Only one month had passed since our first baby would have been due and our second baby had miscarried. How could he even suggest such a thing? All my pent-up pain gushed out in angry sobs. Slamming the door to our bedroom, I buried my head in my pillow and wept tears of fury—toward Ken, toward my in-laws, toward the baby, and toward God.

"Why couldn't it be me?" I screamed at God. "Why did You allow me to miscarry, and yet You gave them a healthy baby girl?" Even as I said the words, I knew I was jealous, and I knew it was wrong. But I didn't care. I wanted to feel sorry for myself and cry until the pain drained away.

All week the upcoming weekend remained an explosive subject. Ken didn't have the heart to disappoint his family, yet my threatened rage weighed heavily on his mind. Apparently there was no hope for agreement between both parties. He would have to make a choice. Finally he decided that it would be best if he went without me. He would explain why I felt uncomfortable coming, and I could stay home as I wished to do.

I consented unhappily. Although it was a relief not to

be going, I had secretly hoped that Ken would stay home to comfort me. Also, the fact that I was left with no transportation upset me even more.

After Ken left I had time to think about my anger, to reevaluate my feelings toward my miscarriage. I even spoke about them to my mother. I was surprised at the intensity of my reaction to the birth of a baby. Had I not recovered from my grief at all? What kind of wife and Christian was I if I could act so hatefully? Shame filtered its way through my anger and self-pity. I still had a lot of healing to do.

When Ken returned Sunday night, I apologized for my explosion and asked him if he had had a good time with his family. Surprisingly, he said the visit had been much more difficult than he had expected. Seeing the newborn in his brother's arms reminded Ken of the sharp reality that he might never have his own baby to hold. At that moment he became aware of just how much he had missed when we went through our miscarriages. Until then he'd had only a glimpse of understanding the enormity of our loss.

So the trip ended up being a blessing in disguise. I had been forced to work through some hidden envy and anger I didn't even know existed, and Ken had gained an invaluable insight into comprehending my grief and his own. Both of us came away from the experience stronger and more determined to be supportive of one another. Now I understood why God had permitted Ken's brother to call—it was another opportunity for Him to heal our broken hearts.

The following week a friend called to tell me about a baby shower that was being planned. Determined not to make the same mistake twice, I drew in a deep breath and assured her I would be happy to go in with her on a gift. I was certain God could get me through the baby shower.

Then my friend suggested that she could send the gift with someone else, and the two of us could go out to a nice restaurant and get a bite to eat. "I thought the shower might be too hard on you," she said, "so I thought supper out might be the perfect remedy!"

Tears of gratitude filled my eyes. "Yes, I think that would be a great idea! And thank you so much for understanding." She would never realize the great impact that one gesture of kindness had on me.

God had known what was best for me all along.

Chapter 15

PROFESSIONAL TREATMENTS

We have small troubles for a while now, but they are helping us gain an eternal glory that is much greater than the troubles. 2 Cor. 4:17, NCV.

Not long after my second miscarriage, Ken and I decided to see a fertility specialist. We were afraid to try for another baby until we determined the cause of my miscarriages. While we waited anxiously for our rescheduled appointment, we discovered that our insurance would pay for some of the expenses in seeing a specialist. Another blessing from God!

Finally the anticipated day arrived. The nurses took a medical history on each of us—information on lifestyles, diseases, and reasons for death of family members. When the doctor reviewed the questionnaire, he seemed especially concerned about my family. A distant relative had experienced several miscarriages before having both normal and mentally disabled children.

Because both of my losses had occurred before the first trimester, he suggested that genetic errors were likely the cause. Only by conducting genetic testing on both Ken and me would he know about my chances of having another miscarriage or a child with a disability. This process would be very expensive and would have to be done at a hospital. Each of us would have blood drawn and sent to a laboratory for study. We would not find out the results for a month.

Although there were other tests the specialist recommended, this one worried me the most. What would I do if the results showed that something was genetically wrong with me? I didn't want to bring a child into the world who would suffer from a disability. Could this be why I had miscarried? I longed to know the answer to that question, but the cost of the test prevented us from making any hasty decisions.

We finally decided to proceed, agreeing that if something was seriously wrong with either of us, we would discontinue our efforts to get pregnant.

My heart quickened as the technician casually stuck the needle into my arm. All my dreams of having a baby were contained in that tube of blood. Ken and I walked to the elevator hand in hand, not saying a word.

Taking a deep breath, I stammered, "If there is something wrong with me genetically, I could have my tubes tied, and if something happened to me, you could remarry and still have children."

He was too surprised to answer for a moment, but at last he replied slowly, "Well, I guess that would be all right with me."

He hadn't noticed the tears in my eyes, and of course he couldn't see the pain and guilt that pierced my soul. Unreasonable thoughts whirled around in my mind, and I found myself powerless to resist them. Somehow I felt responsible, even though there was nothing I could do. Maybe Ken would eventually wish he had married someone else. I knew he loved children. Would he resent me later?

The trip home was silent, but inside I screamed, *Please, God, just let me be normal!*

Toward the end of this long month of waiting I met with the women's group that had brought me such strength and encouragement. They'd all been praying for me, and I'm sure their prayers had helped me keep my sanity during the suspense. As we met together that night, studying God's Word and praying, I felt as though God were speaking directly to me. He gently reminded me it was not *my* responsibility to get pregnant, or to find more jobs to pay the bills, or to make my tests come out normal. My *only* responsibility was to trust Him, and let Him take control of my life. He would fulfill the longings of my heart and make me happy. That was *His* job! My happiness depended not on having a baby but in trusting God. With tears of joy in my eyes I shared with the ladies that even if I never became pregnant or had a baby, God would fulfill my need for children. He had a thousand ways to make me feel complete as a woman, where I had only one. I had only to trust Him!

During this month I also discovered I was one of many in the quest of a normal pregnancy. I found that 10 million persons in the United States (15 percent of the childbearing population) have fertility problems. And if one includes miscarriages, the figure rises to 17 percent. About one out of 10 couples who have one child are unable to conceive others.*

Like many women struggling with infertility, I had plenty of time to reflect on all the testing and treatments I had received thus far. The doctors had been unsure of my chances of becoming pregnant because so little was known about a bilateral teratoma tumor. They performed many treatments and tests in the hope of learning why I couldn't conceive easily, and why I miscarried when I did.

I began by taking my basal body temperature every morning, then charting the readings on a graph so the doctor could tell when I was ovulating. A woman's body temperature builds until around day 14 of her cycle, when she ovulates and her temperature suddenly rises two or three degrees. It is at this surge that one is most likely to conceive. After the surge the temperature will level off for a while, and then drop (which means the woman will most likely begin her period), or remain the same (signaling possible pregnancy). I had been charting my temperature both times I had become pregnant. However, as month after month passed and I was unable to conceive again, the graphing only made me more discouraged.

I was also taking Clomid, a fertility drug to help me ovulate regularly. According to the basal body temperature charts, I often skipped months. I had been taking this drug for a year and a half before I became pregnant the first time. After my second miscarriage almost a year later, new research revealed that Clomid could cause ovarian cancer if a woman were on it more than a year. The continual use of medication was causing the lining of my uterus to become thinner, which could cause problems in the attachment of the embryo, possibly resulting in another miscarriage. The specialist assured me he could give me progesterone to help build the uterus lining, but sometimes I wondered if the treatment was more dangerous than anyone thought. In reality, no one knew all the effects of treating infertility, because not enough research had yet been done.

Another concern for me was the possibility of my remaining tube being blocked by scar tissue from my surgeries. To ease my worry, the doctor ordered a hysterosalpingogram (HSG). I was admitted to the hospital and taken to the Radiology Department, where I was hooked up to an X-ray machine and a TV monitor. A radiopaque dye was expelled into my cervix and uterine cavity and allowed to pass through my tube. I watched the whole procedure on the TV screen, well aware of the pressure and cramping of my uterus. For a few awful moments nothing happened. The radiologist ordered more pressure, and the cramping grew worse. Suddenly the dye snaked through the S-shaped tube, and everyone sighed in relief and smiled. My tube was open. Pregnancy was possible.

Although most of the tests were done on me, Ken didn't escape. He had to bring in a sperm specimen for a semen analysis that would allow the specialists to get an accurate count of sperm and their ability to move through the uterus. The test would also show how many deformed or underdeveloped sperm were present. Even though a normal man produces millions of sperm, mobility or development may be poor. The actual sperm count may not be high enough, which can sometimes cause problems of infertility.

Ken's analysis came back normal. I had almost hoped it wouldn't. Guilty as I felt, I didn't want to be the sole problem. No test had yet shown why either one of us was experiencing any difficulty in conceiving a child. No reason for miscarriage had been discovered. Although both of us were thankful we were "normal," we were frustrated that the problem had not been solved.

Three months after our second miscarriage, Ken and I started trying to get pregnant again. I had originally thought I might not have much trouble, since I had conceived the first month we tried after my first miscarriage. But when month after month passed, our dreams began to evaporate.

I visited the infertility clinic each month to see if the fertility drugs were overstimulating my ovaries. I got to know the doctors and nurses by name and determined to be more positive and pleasant when I went for my appointments. However, I often battled with feelings of resentment (because of the great cost) and defeat (because the treatments weren't working). The very sight of the infertility clinic depressed me.

One day as I was sitting in the waiting room, the word "fertile" triggered my memory of a conversation I had had with a casual acquaintance. At the mention of my miscarriages and my inability to get pregnant, she laughed and motioned to her six children, saying, "I wish I had that problem! My husband calls me 'fertile Myrtle'!"

I cringed, but tried to smile at her not-so-funny quip. I knew she hadn't meant to hurt me, yet I was amazed at how easily a stab of pain resulted from a careless word.

---

*Vicky Love, *Childless Is Not Less* (Minneapolis: Bethany House Publishers, 1984), pp. 14, 15.

Chapter 16

ACCEPTANCE

*With a loud command and with the shout of the chief angel and a
blast of God's trumpet, the Lord will return from heaven. Then
those who had faith in Christ before they died will be raised to life.
Next, all of us who are still alive will be taken up into the clouds
together with them to meet the Lord in the sky. From that time on
we will all be with the Lord forever. Encourage each other
with these words. 1 Thess. 4:16, 17, CEV.*

Even though I had given my longing for a child to the
Lord, my emotions still roller-coastered up and
down. I struggled with depression and the total surrender of control to His plans. One day I heard a
radio minister describe depression as "anger at God turned
inward," a form of distrusting the Lord. This surprised me,
since I was sure I had resolved my anger. Then I began to
realize that anger (as well as any other step in the grieving
process) could return, although not with the same intensity. If I truly believed God had my best interest in mind,
why should I worry about the past or the future? Didn't
He have my life in His nail-pierced hands? How could He
prove His love more completely than in dying for me? I
certainly didn't understand His ways. But then no human
can fully comprehend the Lord's leading, because we can't

see the end from the beginning (Isa. 55:8, 9).

I did believe God could answer some of the burning questions that haunted my heart. Perhaps this would enable me to release my depression and let His love completely heal the hurt. Most of all, I longed to understand what had actually happened to my children, and if I'd ever see them again. Where were my babies now?

My neighbor insisted my children were in heaven, cherubs around the throne of God. But this belief brought me little comfort. How could a loving God take away my babies to be two of His numerous angels in heaven? That wouldn't be fair or considerate! This theory contradicted the picture of Christ's love that I had discovered in Isaiah. I decided to study for myself the subject of death, according to the Bible. Surely God would provide the answers in His Word.

The more I studied, the more excited I became. The mystery of death seemed to unfold before my eyes. I was surprised to discover how important the knowledge about death and the resurrection (being raised from the dead) was to the Christian. In fact, if one does not believe in the resurrection of the dead, the apostle Paul says his/her faith is "empty" or "futile"! (1 Cor. 15:13-17, NKJV).

Evidently, God does not deal lightly with this subject. In the same chapter (verse 18) Paul continues by saying that if there is no resurrection, then the dead would "perish," or even cease to exist. So without the belief in the resurrection, the Christian would have no hope of life after death.

But what kind of resurrection is the Bible talking about? Were my babies' spirits floating around in heaven without physical bodies? I had heard that my children's "immortal souls" went straight to heaven at death. As I compared text with text, I discovered the Bible's meaning of the "immortal soul."

I found that God is immortal. In 1 Timothy 1:17 the Bible says, "Now to the King eternal, *immortal,* invisible, to God who alone is wise, be honor and glory forever and ever" (NKJV).

But what about the dead? Could they also be considered immortal? In speaking of Jesus Christ, Paul states, "God, the blessed and only Ruler, the King of kings and Lord of lords, who alone is immortal" (1 Tim. 6:15, 16, NIV). According to this text only God has immortality. So why do so many people speak of the "immortal soul"?

First, one must define what immortal means. According to the dictionary, immortal is defined as "one exempt from death." I could understand then why only God is immortal. There was no question that my babies had died, so they could not be referred to as immortal. In fact, I could find no reference in the Bible for an immortal soul. According to one scholar, the Bible uses the word "soul" 1,600 times, but never once uses "immortal soul."[1]

I discovered the biblical definition of "soul" in Genesis, the first book of the Bible. God created a "living soul" when He breathed into Adam the breath of life. "And the Lord God formed man of the dust of the ground, and breathed into his nostrils the *breath of life;* and man became a living soul" (Gen. 2:7). According to this text, the "dust of the ground" plus the "breath of life" equaled the "living soul." I knew that Adam eventually died (Gen. 5:5), so he could not have had an immortal soul. He was made out of dust, and God told him "to dust you will return" (Gen. 3:19, NIV). Since the "breath of life" was taken away at death and his body became dust, Adam, as a soul, ceased to exist. "The soul who sins shall die" (Eze. 18:20, NKJV). Evidently, having a soul does not make a person immortal or exempt from death.

Then what, exactly, happens to the soul at death? Ecclesiastes 12:7: "The dust [body] returns to the ground it came from, and the *spirit* returns to God who gave it" (NIV). At death the body becomes dust, and the spirit returns to God.

But what is the spirit? Is it some ghost flying around in heaven without a body? Job states, "All the while my *breath* is in me, and the *spirit* of God is in my nostrils" (Job 27:3). The "spirit" is the "breath of life" that God breathed into Adam when he became a *living soul.*

Therefore, a living soul consists of the physical body that God formed out of the dust, and the breath of life (spirit) that God grants to each human being. When a person dies, the body returns to dust, and the spirit, or breath of life, returns to God.

This spirit, or breath of God, is not a separate, living identity. According to Psalm 115:17 the dead cannot praise God. "The dead praise not the Lord, neither any that go down into silence." David also believed the dead would not be able to remember or give the Lord thanks. In Psalm 6:5 he states, "No one remembers [God] when he is dead" (NIV). David also says, "His spirit departs, he returns to his earth; *in that very day* his plans perish" (Ps. 146:4, NKJV). The departed soul has no thinking ability. The very day that he dies, all thoughts "perish."

Could it be possible that I might be able to communicate with my dead babies before the resurrection at Jesus' second coming? The previous texts imply that communication with the dead is not possible, but in Ecclesiastes 9:5, 6 the Bible clearly states, "The living know that they will die, but the *dead know nothing. . . .* Their love, their hate and their jealousy have long since vanished; never again will they have a part in anything that happens under the sun"

(NIV). When someone dies, he/she has no existence. This text clearly states that my babies are not aware of anything; therefore, communication is impossible.

So what are my children doing now? God's Word plainly teaches that the dead are simply sleeping. In 1 Thessalonians 4 Paul refers to the dead as "those who have fallen asleep" (verses 13 and 14, NIV). Jesus also refers to death as a "sleep" in Luke 8:52, 53 and John 11:11-14. The Bible refers to death as a sleep more than 50 times.[2] Therefore, my dead babies must be asleep, waiting for the resurrection.

When will the resurrection occur? The Bible is definite about this. Paul comforts the loved ones who have lost their friends and family in death by saying, "The Lord Himself will descend from heaven with a shout, with the voice of an archangel, and with the trumpet of God. And the dead in Christ will rise first" (1 Thess. 4:17, NKJV). The dead are raised at Christ's second coming and receive immortality. "We will not all sleep, but we will all be changed . . . at the last trumpet. . . . The dead will be raised imperishable. . . . And the mortal with immortality" (1 Cor. 15:51-53, NIV). At the Second Coming the resurrected dead are given "glorious" bodies, like Christ's glorified body (Phil. 3:21, NIV). Christ appeared to His disciples after His resurrection from the dead and His return from heaven, saying, "Look at my hands and my feet. It is I myself! Touch me and see; a ghost does not have flesh and bones" (Luke 24:39, NIV). Likewise, those who die and are resurrected will have the same kind of bodies. My babies are not spirits; they will have flesh and bones, and I will be able to hold them in my arms!

Will my babies go to heaven before me? Both the redeemed who are alive at the Second Coming and the resurrected dead will go to God *at the same time.* "Then we who are alive and remain shall be caught up *together with them* [the resurrected dead] in the clouds to meet the Lord in the air. And thus we shall always be with the Lord" (1 Thess. 4:17, NKJV).

How exciting! My children lay sleeping until the Second Coming; *they were not in heaven looking down at my suffering!* At the resurrection Jesus will awaken my little ones from their sleep, and *together* we will spend eternity with Him!

This essential truth of the Bible brought tears of joy to my eyes. I now had God's promise that I would be reunited with my precious children! The apostle summarized my newfound joy by saying, "Therefore comfort one another with these words" (verse 18, NKJV).

God is my strength. His Word is sure. Someday I will hold my children in my arms—just as He promises! The assurance I found by studying the subject of death helped my comprehension of texts such as Romans 8:28: "And we know that in all things God works for the good of those who love him" (NIV). The apostle Paul had been beaten, stoned, and imprisoned when he wrote these words, but he still held fast to his faith in God's ability to reverse bad situations.

What a wonderful promise! As I trust God and remain true to His plan for my life, I look forward to the day when I *will* understand His ways and see the good in the tragedy. "No matter how our soul's enemy attacks or human circumstances impact our lives, God can ultimately take the pain or problem, redeem it, and use it for our good. What Satan planned for evil, God can turn for good."[3]

Some blessings had come from my miscarriages, although it took me a while to recognize them. The very fact that I was able to become pregnant was in itself a miracle, considering I had only one tube and one fourth of an ovary left. And this small piece of ovary was there only because a doctor had saved it by performing emergency surgery on a strangled hernia when I was 6 months old. Since the two surgeries no doctor could tell me if my ovary was producing eggs. Now I had proof. The ovary had to be functional in order for me to have become pregnant. This fact gave me great encouragement and hope for having another baby.

Second, even though my husband and I had experienced problems in coping with our babies' deaths, overall we had developed a deeper relationship. Through the miscarriages we learned how to communicate our feelings better, share in each other's pain, and grow from the trials we were experiencing. Perhaps there is some truth to the saying, "Tragedy either makes or breaks a couple." Fortunately, the trials seemed to strengthen our marriage and bond us closer than we had been before.

Finally, the loneliness I had experienced as a result of my miscarriage convinced me that I needed some kind of support group. I had read about support groups that were specifically designed for mothers who had lost children. Several books listed the names, addresses, and phone numbers of these organizations. A few of these are listed below:

The Miscarriage and Stillbirth Support Group
Dorothy Hai
209 York St.
Olean, New York 14760
(716) 375-2111 or (716) 372-7021

HAND (Helping After Neonatal Death)
c/o Barbara Jones
P.O. Box 3805
San Anselmo, California 94960

EASE (Empty Arms Support Effort)
Mary Beth Donnelly
607 E. Olive
Bloomington, Illinois 61401

All these organizations sounded helpful, but I felt they were too far away from where I was located. However, I did long for this type of encouragement. I needed to know that other women had experienced what I was going through and had survived.

This desire eventually compelled me to become more active in my church. There I met many other women who had been through similar tragedies. I was able to talk to several of them and ask how they had lived through their calamities, what had brought them comfort, and what they would have done differently if they could. Several suggested Christian books or Bible verses that had been especially meaningful. As a result of my loss I realized the importance of developing deeper relationships within my church family.

Studying God's Word renewed my hope and continued to heal my hurt. Even though memories would pop back into my mind without warning, their biting sting had softened. In its place grew acceptance. Acceptance of death as part of living. Acceptance of pain as part of growth. Acceptance of God's plan for my life instead of my own. As acceptance budded, my faith and hope returned. I could smile and laugh and sing again—not because I felt free of pain, but because I was living through it with peace and assurance.

I sometimes imagined Jesus longing for the day when He could breathe into my babies the breath of life. I could almost see Him smiling at the thought of waking them up. I could almost hear His tender voice reassuring me that my little ones would one day be laughing in my arms. Whether or not this daydream helped speed my healing process, I don't know. Knowing that my children lay asleep in Jesus' care brought me great comfort. I couldn't wait for the day when I would be reunited with them for eternity. This hope gave me strength each morning. It was on this promise that my faith rested and peace reigned.

When I felt depression sneaking back into my soul, I would drop to my knees for help. I had to agree that "disappointment can be a catalyst for a renewed dependence on God."[4] As I felt my strength ebbing, I would lean heavily on Jesus' strong arms. He never failed to hold me if I gave Him permission. Even during the times that Satan threatened to rip the delicate threads of hope from my heart, my eyes would lift toward heaven. Though sometimes I couldn't feel His presence, I knew Jesus was near. He would never fail me.

Rainy days and darkness were especially difficult, since they reminded me of the day of my miscarriage. Since evenings were especially hard for me, I started a regular Bible reading time at night. I sang songs and studied the Bible and other good devotional books, some written specifically for women, in the morning and at night.

One day as I was reading my Bible, I came across Luke 4:18. Speaking of Jesus, the text read, "The Spirit of the Lord is upon Me, because He has . . . sent Me to heal the brokenhearted" (NKJV). I thought, *A little at a time, I can feel my heart being pieced back together. Thank You, Lord. You really are the Great Physician!*

One Tuesday evening I found myself debating whether or not I should go to prayer meeting. It had been an exceptionally hard day, and I was tired. Part of me longed to curl up in my rocking chair with a good book and try to forget the hassles of the past few hours. But the other part insisted that I go to church. Somehow I dragged myself reluctantly to the car and drove to prayer meeting. As I sat down in the pew, my tiredness lessened. I always enjoyed the service once I got there. And in this particular meeting I would gain more than I had expected.

The topic for the night's discussion was the names of God. The pastor told the story of Abram's burning desire to have a son. He literally begged God to keep His promise of a child, even though Sarai was much too old to conceive. Abram referred to God as Adonai, who keeps promises (Gen. 15:2, 8). Those words kept ringing in my mind: *Adonai, the promise keeper.* Wasn't God the same promise keeper today as He was in Abram's days? Wasn't He keeping His promises to me? Words flooded into my mind, and I began scribbling them down on paper. As I drove home God gave me a special melody for the verses I had written. I sang:

> I come before the Father,
> With a song inside my heart,
> Knowing that His promises are true.
> I kneel before the altar,
> Asking how to do my part.
> Such perfect peace He gives me to endure.
>
> For my God is a promise keeper,
> His covenant is sure; His commitment never fails.
> I will lift up my heart's desire,
> Knowing I can trust in Him, my Saviour and my Friend.
> He pledges me His love, and seals it with His blood.
> Adonai, You are the promise keeper.

There are times that I might wonder,
And be tempted to ask why.
Trials try to sever me from You.
But Lord, You know the future,
And Your hand holds fast to mine.
Help me keep my promises to You.

Perhaps your heart is heavy,
And you long to find it rest.
Broken vows have shattered all your dreams.
Jesus is the answer,
He can fill your emptiness.
His love is stronger than your greatest need.

At home I put guitar chords with the words I'd written. The following week I sang the song at prayer meeting, relating my experience to the congregation. God had given me yet another blessing from my miscarriage—a chance to praise Him—and in return He had blessed me with His joy.

Satan had tried his best to prevent me from attending prayer meeting that night. What a tragedy it would have been to miss such a blessing!

"Dear Jesus," I prayed, "please help me somehow to show Your glory through my pain. I know You understand my feelings, for You once suffered here on earth too. Always keep a song in my heart, Lord, because I am not strong enough at times to sing. I know You are the promise keeper. Just help me keep my promises to You."

[1] Mark Finley, *Studying Together* (Fallbrook, Calif.: Hart Research Center, 1991), p. 49.
[2] *Ibid.*
[3] J. Hayford, *I'll Hold You in Heaven,* p. 82.
[4] P. Vredevelt, *Empty Arms,* p. 25.

Chapter 17

ENCOUNTER

*"And God will wipe away every tear from their eyes; there
shall be no more death, nor sorrow, nor crying. There shall be no
more pain, for the former things have passed away." Rev. 21:4, NKJV.*

The Lord immediately began answering my
prayers for happiness and peace in the most
surprising way. I would never have dreamed
that a simple encounter could make such an
impact on my life.

It began the weekend I attended a seminar presented
by Donna Stein. She stressed that Christians should ask
God specifically for what they need. Then God will show
them why trials are necessary, and how these experiences
will benefit them. I had never considered asking for reasons and benefits of my trials. The concept was refreshing.
Only a few minutes passed before I had the perfect opportunity to see if her ideas would work.

In the bathroom during an intermission, I bumped into
a friend who was taking care of her baby girl—the same
friend who had discovered she was pregnant with her
third child only a month after I became pregnant.
Hurriedly I brushed by her, saying a quick hello, then I literally hid in a stall, hoping she would leave. I had managed

to avoid her for many months since she had given birth, even though we had gotten together often before our pregnancies. I knew she wondered why I hadn't called, but it was too hard to explain. So I did the next-best thing—*I hid.*

As I pondered my escape, a memory of a few days before flashed into my mind. I had been shopping at the mall for a baby's gift. It wasn't the first time; many friends had had babies. It was simply one of those chores that needed to be done. Usually I could have paid the cashier and taken the gift home without too much thought. But not that day. For some reason the pain had slashed my heart so deeply that I had run to my car and burst into tears. For a long time I sat there, mourning over the babies I had lost.

Now those same feelings washed over me again. I didn't want to see *any* baby, especially one so close in age to what my own would have been. Suddenly I remembered the speaker's message. She had said to ask God *specifically* for my needs. Well, right now I needed to get out of the bathroom. However, my friend could be waiting for me, since we hadn't seen each other in such a long time. What would I say? How could I survive talking to her without bursting into tears? I bowed my head quickly and prayed, *Lord, I'm tired of hiding from the pain. I need peace when I see a baby or baby things. In fact, I want to feel joy, just as I used to before I became pregnant.*

It was a strange request, but I was in a strange situation. I really didn't feel any different than I had before I prayed. I wondered if the prayer was really appropriate or if it would help at all. Seconds clicked away, and it was becoming obvious I had been in the bathroom stall for a very long time. I bravely opened the door and walked out.

My heart was pounding as I saw my friend smile and pick up her baby. As our eyes met, I remembered a conversation we had had when she was only a few months pregnant. She had asked my permission to name her baby Melisa (the Spanish version of my name) if it was a girl. Of course I was flattered and had said yes.

Now I was face-to-face with my namesake. The little girl stared at me with deep dark eyes. I couldn't believe how much she had grown! Enchanted, I walked to her and smiled as I reached down and tickled the bottom of her tiny feet. I suddenly realized I wasn't hurting inside. I felt nothing. No pain. No joy. Only peace.

Later that day I noticed the same friend sitting alone at a table and decided to go talk to her. She acted thrilled that I showed renewed interest in our friendship and invited me to sit down. I hesitated, wondering if the serenity I had felt in the bathroom could last. After a few minutes of small talk, she asked if I would be willing to hold Melisa while she got something to eat. Before I could stammer a response, she handed over her precious little bundle. As I took the small child in my arms, tears threatened to spill over. In desperation I cried out for God's help. Then I looked down at the baby's face, and she smiled, quite content to snuggle up to me. She closed her eyes, looking so peaceful there in my arms.

"I think you're sleepy," I murmured, more to myself than to her. In that moment a thought flashed into my mind. Jesus was holding me, just as I was holding my little namesake! Suddenly I was aware of the peace flowing out of my heart, followed by a brand-new emotion, one I hadn't experienced in a very long time: joy! Just what I had prayed for!

I smiled at the sleeping babe and whispered, "Rest now, my precious Melisa." And in my heart I could hear God's whisper echoing the same words back to me.

~ ~ ~

A few days later the phone rang. The hospital laboratory technician was on the other end of the line. My heartbeat tripled as I realized this was the moment I'd been waiting for all month. In some ways my entire future lay in this technician's report. I wondered if he had any idea the impact his words would have.

"Mrs. Hanson, the genetic tests that you and your husband took have come back normal. There should be no cause for concern in trying to conceive a healthy child."

Tears rushed from my eyes as I stammered a quick thank you and hung up the phone. I realized I had been holding my breath throughout the entire conversation and let it out in a great sigh of relief.

"Praise God!" I repeated again and again, thanking Him for working this miracle in my life. I couldn't wait to tell Ken that we still had hope. God had made certain of that! "Thank You, Lord! Thank You!"

~ ~ ~

Soon after I found out the results of the genetic tests, the Christmas season arrived. I had been so preoccupied with the test results that I had barely noticed the merry lights or the spirit of the holidays. Now I happily decorated my home and sang Christmas carols with renewed enthusiasm. Was it only last year that I had been pregnant with my first child? Time had passed so quickly, and another Christmas had nearly arrived. I decided not to let my bittersweet memories spoil the holidays. After all, at least pregnancy was still possible! A month earlier I didn't have even that assurance!

As I baked Christmas cookies and hung up my wreath,

I had time to reflect on the past year. Experiencing two miscarriages only six months apart had been a struggle, no doubt about it. Yet God had been faithful. He had not forsaken Ken and me in our sorrow and pain. With the coming of a new year our hopes and dreams were renewed. True, I didn't know what the future would hold, but I did know the One who holds the future! With this assurance I looked forward to facing the challenges and joys of the upcoming days, determined to trust God with my job, my husband, my children, and my life. Whatever lay ahead could not separate me from His love.

Chapter 18

WAITING

Wait on the Lord; be of good courage, and He shall strengthen your heart; wait, I say, on the Lord! Ps. 27:14, NKJV.

January came, and then February. The anniversary of my first miscarriage passed, and we waited, hoping each month that I would get pregnant again. March rolled by, followed by April, May, June, July, and August. Every month we prayed for a baby. Every month my period began.

In September my doctor suggested we go to a stronger fertility drug, Metrodin. We attended a class on how to prepare the medicine, and Ken learned the technique of giving me a shot. On days three through seven of my cycle, Ken injected the medicine between 4:00 and 6:00 p.m. I returned to the fertility clinic for a sonogram to see how big my egg follicles had grown. The nurse counted how many follicles I had produced and measured the diameter of each. My blood was drawn to determine how long it would be until I would ovulate. After the results from both tests had been discussed with the doctor, either I would be instructed to continue the shots and repeat the entire procedure in a few days, or I would be given HCG hormone to force my body to ovulate within the next day.

If the second option were advised, then I would have to bring in a semen sample to be injected into my uterus 36 hours after ovulation. After the insemination I would be given a shot of progesterone to build the lining of my uterus and be told to take one pill every night until either I had a period or found out I was pregnant.

The process was long and tedious. My entire life revolved around getting pregnant. Not even work could interfere with the correct timing. I wondered if all of the scheduling problems were worth it, especially after a month had passed and I hadn't become pregnant. Ken hated giving me so many shots. However, since the shots were natural hormones, my uterine lining would not be affected. This fact comforted me as I felt the stab of yet another injection.

Financially we couldn't afford to continue with these treatments very long, and emotionally we couldn't long withstand the mental agony we experienced when they failed. We had to agree on a cutoff date. Perhaps it was not God's will for us to get pregnant. Were we being good stewards of our money if this were the case?

December was chosen as the final date, two full years from the time I had become pregnant with our first child. If we were not pregnant by then, we would begin the process to adopt a child.

Ken was much more agreeable to adoption than I. He often teased me about going to Mexico and coming back with a little black-eyed girl with long eyelashes and dark hair. He swore no one would ever know she wasn't ours, since she would look so much like me. I would smile and nod my head. I had always wanted a little girl who looked like me. I had grown up being told how much I resembled my mother. I never minded—she was beautiful in my eyes. For as long as I could remember, I had pictured myself with my own little girl.

Perhaps that was one reason I hesitated to adopt. It wasn't just looks, but the entire gene pool would be different. Maybe my adopted child and I would be nothing alike. Maybe we wouldn't even get along. My mother and I had always been so close. I couldn't imagine not having that kind of relationship with my daughter.

Another major consideration was the great expense and the long wait. We had been told that adoption could cost between $5,000 and $10,000.

Disease was another concern. What if the child had AIDS or had been brain-damaged from drugs or alcohol taken by the mother?

And what if the mother changed her mind at the last minute and didn't give us her baby? Or, worse, what if she came back years later and tried to take the child away from us? Could I accept that risk? I wasn't sure.

On the other hand, adoption would fill my need for children, and perhaps God could use me to love a child who was unwanted. Several years earlier Ken and I had taken a 7-year-old boy into our home for several months while his mother was in a mental hospital. The child had such a sweet disposition and gentle nature that I grew to think of him as my own. I would have eagerly adopted him if the option had been available. Perhaps God would find a child I couldn't help but love.

All we could do was wait. If I hadn't conceived by December, we would assume God wanted us to adopt. Although I pleaded daily with God to give me a child of my own, I finally chose to do His will, even if it meant adopting—or never having children at all. It was a difficult decision, resulting from a terrific inner battle, but as I surrendered I found what I was searching for—peace.

Tears trickled down my cheeks as I meditated on Galatians 4:4-7. God gently reminded me He had adopted *me* as part of *His* family. The words penetrated deeply into my heart. "When the fullness of the time had come, God sent forth His Son, born of a woman, born under the law, to redeem those who were under the law, that we might receive the adoption as sons. And because you are sons, God has sent forth the Spirit of His Son into your hearts, crying out, 'Abba, Father!' Therefore you are no longer a slave but a son, and if a son, then an heir of God through Christ" (NKJV). If God had been willing to adopt me, could I refuse to adopt a child if it were His plan for my life? I prayed, "O Lord, You adopted me, a lowly sinner, as Your own daughter. Make me willing to love someone else's child as You love me."

~ ~ ~

I have never considered myself to be a patient person. My prayer for long-suffering was "Lord, make me patient—and please *hurry!*" God, however, was answering my prayer—on His time frame, not mine.

The monthly women's meetings continued to give me the support I needed to survive. Sometimes I could almost feel the prayers of the members when I was faced with discouraging circumstances. I no longer focused only on my pain, but I learned to pray for my friends who were facing different trials in their lives. I shared with them some verses that had become especially meaningful to me as I searched the Bible for comfort and strength. The texts that helped me surrender to God my longing for children included:

Luke 11:9-13: Ask and I will receive. The Father gives only good gifts.

Psalm 116:1, 2: God has heard my supplications.

Psalm 84:11: No good thing will He withhold from me if I walk uprightly.

Psalm 37:4: God will give me the desires of my heart.

Psalm 9:9, 10: He will not forsake me when I seek Him.

Psalm 145:18-20: God fulfills my desires if I call upon Him.

Deuteronomy 4:29: If I seek the Lord, I will find Him.

Jeremiah 29:11-13: God gives me peace, hope, and a future.

Matthew 7:7, 8: If I ask according to His will, it will be given to me.

John 14:14: I must ask in Christ's name, and He will do it.

John 16:24: By asking, I will be filled with joy.

Romans 8:32: He will freely give me all things.

Philippians 4:19: He supplies all my needs.

Hebrews 10:23: If I hold fast to hope, He who promises it is faithful.

James 1:17: Every good gift is from God.

1 John 5:14, 15: God hears and answers my prayers.

Each of these texts brought me assurance of God's leading in my life. If I would but trust Him, I would be filled with His peace and joy. As my faith strengthened, He gave me comfort and assurance that I, in turn, could share with others.

One Sabbath at church a man pulled me aside to tell me his daughter had just lost her baby at 6 weeks. As tears formed in his eyes he whispered, "I knew you would understand. I just had to tell you."

I did understand a little of his pain. It had been his first grandchild. We shared a common bond. Although I didn't always say or do the right thing, I did try to listen and empathize, and usually that was enough.

As time passed I learned of other miscarriages, and I

often sent cards with Bible texts and a personalized letter to each of my heartbroken friends. Sometimes I would call. Other times I planned a short visit, whatever I felt would bring comfort. Usually it took only a few minutes, yet it gave me the opportunity to share what God was doing for me and brought encouragement to others.

As December drew near, God was there leading me, strengthening me, giving me encouragement for others. As long as my eyes were on Him, I stayed positive and peaceful.

If only I could keep that focus continually!

Chapter 19

DISAPPOINTMENT BRINGS HOPE

*Call to Me, and I will answer you, and show you great
and mighty things, which you do not know. Jer. 33:3, NKJV.*

A s the end of the month slowly crept by, my
hopes began to rise. If I didn't start my period
within the next few days I would know I was
pregnant. Surely it would be this month!

Then, a few hours later, my dreams of pregnancy
crashed as I began cramping and bleeding. Devastated, I
fell to my knees and sobbed. My peace and assurance
seemed to vanish into the air as I poured out my anger and
frustration with God. Why had He allowed this to happen
just when I was trusting Him more? Would I never get
pregnant? My surrender to God's will was temporarily forgotten as I cried out in pain.

But God did not leave me. Although I raged and
doubted His love, He remained. Almost grudgingly I
reached for my Bible, praying that God would somehow
give me encouragement in His Word. My Bible opened to
2 Kings 4, and immediately I began to grumble that nothing
could be comforting in this book. Then my eyes fell on the

story of the kind Shunammite woman who gave room and board to Elisha and his servant. To repay this woman for her hospitality, Elisha gave her a promise: "About this time next year you shall embrace a son," he said (verse 16, NKJV).

The story seemed to jump to life in front of my eyes, only I was the woman, and God was speaking directly to me! I continued reading.

She replied, "No, my lord. Man of God, do not lie to your maidservant" (verse 16).

Ah, I knew what it was like to doubt God's promises. Sometimes they seemed too good to be true. I was tired of being disappointed. Evidently the Shunammite woman had been too.

God, however, ignored her doubt. His actions did not depend on her feelings or frustrations. The next verse told the amazing evidence of God's love for her: "The woman conceived, and bore a son *when the appointed time had come,* of which Elisha had told her" (verse 17).

Could God be telling me that I, like the Shunammite woman, would have a baby next year, *in His appointed time?* I wasn't sure. It could have been by chance that I had turned to this particular story, although I hadn't read it since I was a child. It could have been coincidence—but I didn't believe so. It was just the encouragement I needed. The exact assurance—and even more than I had asked for or imagined! How good God was! I dried my eyes, and although my cramping and bleeding continued, my heart refused to mourn. God had answered my prayer. I had hope once again.

~ ~ ~

With the onset of my period came another cycle of shots. For a third time I went into the clinic for a sonogram to see if my ovary had any cysts on it. Then more medicine and more shots. Sometimes Ken would accidentally hit a nerve, and pain would shoot up my spine or down my leg. But most of the time I was just sore afterward. My ovary had produced several eggs, but none were big enough when the nurse measured them on the sonogram. So I had to continue with the shots. Although we alternated hips, I could hardly tell the difference, since both were so sore. Ken was having difficulty finding a new place to stick the needle.

Finally I was given permission to take the HCG hormone to stimulate ovulation and then be inseminated. The whole process was at best unpleasant, but necessary. However, we did our best to follow the doctor's instructions.

On the day of the insemination I lay on the examination table, thinking how badly I wanted this process to work. It was almost November. We were running out of time. Again and again I prayed for a baby, but I always added "If it is Your will, Father." I did want His will in my life. He had proved His love for me so many times. I was choosing to trust Him. It was just so hard sometimes.

~ ~ ~

Thanksgiving had almost arrived by the time my period was due. I really hadn't had any signs of pregnancy. I was sure I wasn't pregnant, but I continued to trust and pray. Each day passed slowly, but my period did not begin. Sometimes the medicine could delay a period.

Finally I could stand it no longer and purchased a home pregnancy test. As I waited three minutes for the test results, I couldn't bear to watch. At last I glanced down at the stick. To my amazement, *two lines* met my glance, and my heart jumped for joy. *I was pregnant!* I repeated that phrase again and again in my mind, relishing the words. I wanted to shout them, to sing them. Ken would be thrilled! I couldn't wait to tell him the good news. Then a sobering thought raised its ugly head. *What if I have another miscarriage?* There was always that possibility. What made me think that this pregnancy would be any different from the others?

Once again I remembered the story of the Shunammite woman. God had promised not only that she would *conceive,* but that she would *bear* a child by the following year. God had kept His promise, and I had conceived. Now I would have to trust Him to bring about delivery at the right time.

As the clinic confirmed my pregnancy with a blood test, my spirits soared. *I would have a baby by this time next year!* Nothing could have made me happier! *Oh, thank You, God. Thank You for this precious gift!* Two days later another pregnancy test was done, this time to measure the growth rate of the embryo. If it didn't double every two days, something was wrong, and a miscarriage would likely occur.

As I waited for the results, I had time to ask myself some hard questions. How would I have reacted if the pregnancy test had been negative? Would I still have chosen God's will if He hadn't answered my prayer in the way I wanted? And what about the future? What if the tests came back abnormal? What if I miscarried a third time? What if the doctor couldn't find a heartbeat? Could I still trust God and His plan for my life?

Two days seemed like an eternity. I prayed nearly every time the phone rang. Finally the nurse called with the news. My pregnancy was developing at the correct rate, and everything looked fine. Maybe this time I would have no problems.

Chapter 20

THANKSGIVING

*He gives children to the woman who has none and makes
her a happy mother. Praise the Lord! Ps. 113:9, NCV.*

During the next few days Ken and I struggled
with the difficult decision of when to tell our
family and friends our news. Since Thanksgiving was only a few days away, and we were
celebrating with both of our families, it seemed to be the
perfect opportunity to share such an answer to prayer.
However, I was just a little more than four weeks pregnant. So much could go wrong. Should we risk raising
everyone's hopes?

We finally decided we couldn't keep such good news a
secret, and our families were overjoyed. When my mother
learned I was only four weeks along, I could see the light
in her eyes dim with reservation. For a moment I wondered if I should have waited, but she hurriedly said, "It's
OK, honey. I would have asked you if you were pregnant
anyway. It's just that it's still so early." Disappointment
had stolen her excitement too many times in the past.

"I'm certain I'll be fine this time, Mom." I tried to
sound more confident than I felt as I gave her a reassuring
hug. "We just have to keep praying."

She smiled and nodded, hiding both her tears and fears from me.

Our news seemed to travel with lightning speed. We finally gave up trying to keep quiet and accepted the congratulations from friends and church members. Everyone seemed eager to join in our excitement. Many prayers were also said on our behalf.

Before I knew that I was pregnant, I had been asked to sing Mary's solo in the Christmas cantata. The words of this beautiful lullaby to Baby Jesus while He was still in Mary's womb seemed to fit my situation so perfectly that I was sure God had the timing planned from the beginning. I could relate so well to Mary, not knowing what the future would hold, with no one, except her heavenly Father, really understanding what she was going through.

As I practiced my solo in front of the choir, I pictured Mary and I both singing to our unborn babies. *If you can hear me now, you already know how much I love you. If you can hear me now, you know I need you more than ever. Though I can't hold you in my arms, I can hold you in my heart. And it's just as if we never were apart. Oh, I wonder, if you can hear me now . . .*

Somehow I hoped my baby could know how much I wanted to hold him or her in my arms. I had waited such a long time! As the last note died away, I saw many of the choir members wiping their eyes. Maybe they understood better than I thought.

~ ~ ~

As Christmas neared, the excitement of the holidays absorbed most of my time. Hanging Christmas decorations, shopping for presents, planning the food, and attending Christmas parties made the days fly by. Between the joy of Christmas and the anticipation of a baby, my spirits soared.

I had experienced only mild morning sickness (usually when I didn't eat right on time) and other normal symptoms. All of these signs brought tremendous comfort to me, reassuring me that all was well.

When I went in for my next appointment, I froze in fear when the nurse said she should be able to see the baby's heartbeat on a sonogram. What if she couldn't find one? As I waited for the doctor, I prayed desperately for strength. Over and over, the story of the Shunammite woman ran through my mind: *She will conceive and bear a child . . .* How much these seven words meant to me! All my hopes and dreams seemed to dangle from the end of that simple phrase.

The doctor arrived, and in a moment I saw my child for the first time on the ultrasound. It was so small I had a hard time distinguishing which dark area was my baby. I strained to see something flashing on the screen that would indicate a heartbeat, but could find nothing. Noticing my apparent distress, the nurse immediately directed my gaze to a small form that seemed to be moving. Yes! It seemed to wiggle every few seconds. That movement, the doctor informed me, was the heartbeat.

Relief washed over me, and I began to cry. The harder I tried to stop, the faster the tears came, tears of pure joy. God had answered my prayers. He had given me my heart's desire.

I grasped the sonogram pictures tightly as I left the examination room. The nurses at the front desk asked to see my precious photos, and as I showed them I struggled to hold back my emotions. They must have noticed the redness around my eyes, because they immediately reassured me, offering words of congratulations. If only they knew how much these black-and-white portraits of my baby meant to me. They were tangible proof that God was in the process of creating a miracle inside of me.

During the next week my heart sang with the joy of thanksgiving. My world seemed to be a perfect blend of teaching, writing, being a wife, and, best of all, a *mother*. Happiness spilled over me in a bubbling waterfall of pure delight. Sometimes I wondered if I were the only one who had ever felt so alive and refreshed at the prospects of having a baby. The future held only the fruition of all my hopes and dreams, and I eagerly looked forward to each passing week as being one step closer to holding my precious baby in my arms. Nothing could have prepared me for the days that would follow.

Chapter 21

IN SHOCK

The Lord answers, "Can a woman forget the baby she nurses?
Can she feel no kindness for the child to which she gave birth?
Even if she could forget her children, I will not forget you.
See, I have written your name on my hand." Isa. 49:15, 16, NCV.

Morning sunlight streamed into my bedroom window, welcoming my sixth week of pregnancy. As I rubbed the sleepiness from my eyes, I smiled. The familiar nausea tugged at my stomach, reminding me that baby was demanding a morning feeding. On my way to the kitchen, I stopped by the bathroom and, to my horror, discovered bright-red stains on the tissue paper. Then I stared in disbelief at a pool of blood in the toilet bowl, trying to comprehend what was happening.

I couldn't be having a miscarriage! I had no cramps. I still felt sick at my stomach. All the symptoms of pregnancy were present. There had been no warning, but I could not deny the bleeding, and in my mind it could mean only one thing: I was losing my baby—*again*.

Numbly I called for Ken. Sensing the urgency in my voice, he immediately appeared in the doorway, and one look at my face confirmed that the worst was happening.

We were silent all the way to the doctor's office, too stunned to speak.

I had never bled in my other pregnancies. I tried to find some reason it was happening now. Nothing made sense. I had read too much to be ignorant about the cause of first trimester miscarriages. Most likely something was wrong with the baby. But what? All the tests I'd taken had come back normal. There must be some mistake! This couldn't be happening to me again. Hadn't God promised me this child? I tried to pray, but my thoughts seemed to float in a misty haze, without logic or order.

The clinic had been open only a few minutes by the time Ken and I arrived. The nurses were obviously surprised to see me back so soon.

"I'm bleeding," I said.

I lay down on the examining table, facing the sonogram machine. As I waited, I read what the nurse had typed on the screen: Melissa Hanson, 6 weeks. Then my gaze rested on the computer's cursor. It flashed in a steady rhythm, just like my baby's heartbeat. If only it were still beating, then there would still be hope. . . .

I looked at Ken, sitting quietly. *How can he be so calm?* A part of me admired him for his strength, and the other half was angry at his seeming indifference. *Doesn't he realize how serious this is?*

I asked him to tell me his thoughts and listened guiltily as he told me he'd been praying. He had asked God either to let the baby live as a sign that this pregnancy would continue normally, or to allow the baby to die, so that we would know today there was no hope for the baby's survival.

I trembled. *What if God chooses the latter? Hadn't He allowed me to miscarry the past two times? How could I hope that this pregnancy would be any different?*

The nurse entered the room again. Both doctors had been called out of the clinic, she said, so she would have to do the sonogram. I agreed numbly. Trembling, I lay back down on the table and riveted my eyes to the sonogram machine, desperately begging God for some sign of life. For a moment I couldn't make out any of the dark areas on the screen. The nurse said she was photographing my uterus.

Then suddenly I saw the yolk sack and a tiny dark form resting inside. The screen immediately blurred as I hurriedly brushed away my tears so I could look for movement. Before I could locate the form again, the nurse said matter-of-factly, "There it is."

"There *what* is?" I wanted to scream, but she continued before I could utter a word.

"Do you see it moving? That's the heartbeat. Everything looks fine."

With the flick of a button the picture disappeared. The nurse said I could get dressed, and handed me two more photos of our child. It had all happened so fast my mind seemed to whirl in confusion. *If everything was OK, then why was I bleeding?*

Seeing my confusion, the nurse explained that bleeding is never normal in pregnancy, but it *does* occur sometimes. Either the baby would continue to grow and the bleeding stop, or a miscarriage would result. There was a 50-50 chance either way. However, finding a heartbeat was considerable evidence for hope. Plus, the baby had grown some, so at least for today everything looked fine, though she couldn't guarantee anything about tomorrow or the day after. We'd just have to wait and see.

The nurse at the front desk scheduled me for another sonogram in a week, and we left. How would I ever be able to survive another week without knowing? I collapsed into Ken's arms, sobbing. I didn't know how to feel. Nothing had changed; I could miscarry at any moment. But at least for now I still had hope, even though it was just a tiny strand.

~ ~ ~

Gone were last week's days of joyous ecstasy. The hours dragged by with fear and apprehension. I prayed that the bleeding would stop, but it didn't. The blood had turned a dark brownish color, but it kept coming, drop by drop, menacing and persistent.

I put myself on bed rest, which was very difficult to do, since it was almost Christmas and we had decided to move. My mother came to my rescue and packed nearly everything in our house, cooked, and cleaned so I could remain in bed.

I would never have dreamed that lying down could be so trying. As I looked at the multitude of tasks that lay before me, a feeling of helplessness completely engulfed me. Time was frozen. Every hour that passed seemed just like the one before. I fought a constant battle with depression and boredom. Sometimes when I thought I couldn't stand it any longer, I would reach for my Bible and turn to the story of the Shunammite woman and read it again and again. I had practically memorized it, word for word. It was the only thing that seemed to bring me comfort, and I clung to it as desperately as a mountain climber clutches the last foot of rope. I spent hours talking to God in my mind, reminding Him of His promise, asking Him to help me trust, no matter what. I begged for some understanding as to why this was happening to me. His answer frustrated me nearly as much as the endless bleeding: wait, wait.

At last the long week ended, and I went in for another

sonogram. My heart pounded as I watched the screen for a glimpse of my baby. The doctor showed me the dark area on the sonogram where the blood was coming from in my uterus. Then he focused on the baby. Immediately I could see that it had grown. He assured me the heartbeat was still there, and the baby seemed to be growing at a normal pace. I went home encouraged, but still uncertain.

Every few days I felt like I was beginning to cramp. My back ached continually from all the bed rest, and I got a bad case of constipation and a yeast infection. When I was sure things couldn't get worse, I came down with a severe cold. With each sneeze or cough, pain shot through my abdomen, and I continually feared a miscarriage might result.

A few days before Christmas a close friend called. She had phoned a week earlier to share the exciting news that she was pregnant with her second child. I had wished her well, almost envious of the happiness that bubbled in her voice. Now I sensed that something was seriously wrong. I could guess what had happened before she even got out the words. She had lost the baby. My heart ached for her as memories of my own miscarriages rushed into my mind. There was nothing I could do to ease her pain except cry with her. As I hung up, the fragile hope in my heart seemed to lie shattered in tiny pieces. *Would I miscarry too?*

Somehow I made it through Christmas and enjoyed a short reprieve from the bleeding, only to have it start again. I stifled my disappointment by immersing myself in Isaiah and the Psalms, making a second list of all the texts that brought me comfort. One of my favorite promises came from Isaiah 40:11: "He will feed His flock like a shepherd; He will gather the lambs with His arm, and carry them in His bosom, *and gently lead those who are with young*" (NKJV). Again and again I repeated God's promises.

The next week I had to change doctors. I knew my fertility specialist handled patients only until they became pregnant, then turned them over to their obstetrician. I couldn't bear the thought of returning to the same clinic where I had experienced my past two miscarriages. But I desperately wanted another specialist, so I called the Maternal/Fetal Medicine Department of Wesley Hospital. I would need a written recommendation, they said. Fortunately, my doctor sympathized with my wishes and wrote the letter, even though medically I was not considered of sufficiently high risk to require a specialist.

The days continued to drag by. I finally abandoned the idea of complete bed rest and went back to doing some of my normal activities. It seemed to make little difference in the amount of blood I passed. Every time I went to the bathroom I prayed, "Lord, I'm giving this blood to You. It's Your problem. I can't stop it. I'm giving my worry to You." I had never before known what the Bible meant by surrendering one's will to God every moment. Now I was experiencing it—living in a state of limbo, grasping the last straws of my faith just to keep my sanity.

Chapter 22

NEW FACES

*Trust the Lord with all your heart, and don't depend on
your own understanding. Remember the Lord in all you do,
and he will give you success. Prov. 3:5, 6, NCV.*

I saw my new doctor for the first time when I was 10 weeks pregnant. I had been spotting for more than a month. A nurse ushered me into an examining room and recorded my medical history. While I was still talking, she rolled up my sleeve and proceeded to take my blood pressure.

"Shhh!" she interrupted me. "I'm trying to hear both your heartbeat and the baby's."

Instantly I froze. She could have said that the building was going up in flames and I wouldn't have budged. I waited for what seemed like an eternity, my heart pounding so loudly in my ears that I was sure it must be deafening in hers. As she finished, I asked as casually as I could, "So did you hear it?"

She smiled. "You must be a little nervous, Mrs. Hanson, because your blood pressure is quite high. Just try to relax, and I'll go schedule your sonogram." She abruptly turned and walked out of the room.

Two and a half years before when a nurse could not

find our baby's heartbeat, Ken had been there, and we had eagerly looked forward to that doctor's appointment. I had felt so good. No bleeding. No cramping. Not like now. I had had no reason to worry. Now I could name dozens of reasons. I wished desperately that Ken had come with me this time. How could I face the news alone? All our dreams hung in the balance.

A young technician appeared in the doorway and asked me to lie down on a table next to the large machine that took the sonograms. Silently I obeyed. I flinched as she smeared the jellylike lubricant onto my abdomen, as much from fear as from the cold. She must have seen the dread on my face, because she began asking me about baby names, trying to put me at ease. My eyes, however, were glued to the sonogram screen, where pictures were beginning to form, and I lost track of the conversation.

The forms were much clearer on this machine, and I could easily make out different shapes. Anxiously I waited for the technician to finish photographing my uterus. I knew that at any second she could discover where the pregnancy was implanted. Suddenly the form of the baby flashed onto the screen—the head and body, tiny arms and legs. It seemed to be dancing before my eyes. I returned the technician's smile as she pushed a button that indicated how fast the baby's heart was beating. One hundred forty beats per minute.

"Just right for 10 weeks," she assured me. "And the baby has grown from 24 to 31 millimeters."

The doctor arrived then and finished the examination. She told me there was still blood in my uterus, and I could expect to continue bleeding for at least another week, maybe longer. She didn't know what was causing the bleeding, but hopefully it was just a natural part of the implantation process and would simply go away with time.

"Pregnancies like yours still have a 50-50 chance of miscarriage," she said, "but it's encouraging that the baby seems to be progressing well."

I knew the statistics all too well, yet I was disappointed that after all this time my chances of carrying the baby full-term were not higher.

My doctor assured me that the bleeding would end—if everything was OK. I swallowed hard and didn't ask any more questions. There were no guarantees. However, I would be grateful for today. Today my baby was alive, growing inside me, and I could sing praises to my Lord for answering my prayer. It suddenly occurred to me that I hadn't been alone. An unseen Physician had been beside me the entire time. I bowed my head and thanked Him as I stepped out of the doctor's office into the fresh morning sunshine, determined in my heart that with His strength I would trust Him.

Chapter 23

REFLECTIONS

*He takes care of his people like a shepherd. He gathers
them like lambs in his arms and carries them close to him.
He gently leads the mothers of the lambs. Isa. 40:11, NCV.*

I prayed every day the following week that the bleeding would stop. The flow seemed perhaps a little lighter, and my hopes rose. Then it quit altogether, only to return a couple days later. If the pregnancy were normal, the doctor had said, the bleeding should stop by the end of my first trimester. As the days passed, my prayers grew more urgent and frequent.

One day as I walked out of the bathroom after discovering more blood, my husband noticed the disappointment clouding my expression and quietly said, "Perhaps, Miss, you're praying for the wrong answer. *Maybe you should pray that you bleed even more."*

I looked at him incredulously. How could he say such a thing? Before I could snap back a reply, Ken continued, "I've been praying that the blood will drain out of your uterus and this whole ordeal will end."

Shocked at the impact of his words, I swallowed the retort that had risen in my throat and stared at him. Was it possible that my prayers were only slowing down the process? Could God be waiting on me? The very thought brought my expectations to a screeching halt. As I pondered these questions for the next few days, my prayers took on a different slant. "Lord, I don't know what would be best—only You do. If You want me to bleed, then I guess it's all right with me. Just help me to trust You, Lord, even when I don't understand."

~ ~ ~

It seemed as though all our family, friends, church members, and work associates knew about the complications I was experiencing. Routinely I was asked how I was feeling and if I had quit spotting. Again and again I had to answer, "Not yet, but keep praying."

Our new minister's wife had experienced three miscarriages before delivering two healthy children, so she was a great support for me through these difficult days. Often when I felt like I might lose my mind from worry, I would call her for comfort. She was always willing to pray with me over the phone. Her faithful prayers and those of her husband gave me the strength I needed to face another day of the unknown. Nothing brought me more assurance than the knowledge that so many friends and family were praying for my baby.

One day during this suspenseful time I sat down in my oversized rocking chair and began leafing through my prayer journal. So much had happened since I'd last written in it. I turned the pages back to the day I had discovered I was pregnant. I had been so happy then. I wondered if I'd ever be that happy again.

The future lay ahead of me—so uncertain—yet at that moment God seemed very near. I smiled as I read about my plans for the baby's nursery—Jesus' little lamb. I loved that theme. I could almost picture Jesus cradling my baby in His strong arms, just as He cradled the lamb in the pictures of the Good Shepherd. Words began forming in my mind, and I took out a piece of paper and hastily wrote them down. It was almost as though I could hear Jesus whispering them in my ear, giving me a precious message of encouragement. I began humming a tune and could almost see myself singing this song at my baby's dedication. Feelings of joy and gratefulness swept over me and tears streamed down my cheeks as I finished the last verse. Softly I sang the words that held so much meaning:

Jesus' Little Lamb

Before I ever knew that you were growing inside,
God took a part of me and your dad,
And patiently He formed you and placed you in my womb,
To grow into His perfect little lamb.

You're my baby. My little one
That God has given me to praise His Son.
And as your heart begins to beat,
I will lay you at His feet.
I love you, baby. You're Jesus' little lamb.

As time goes by, God tenderly creates you,
According to His perfect master plan.
And like a gentle shepherd, He meets your growing needs,
And in His arms He cradles His dear lamb.

You're my baby. My little one
That God has given me to praise His Son.
And as I long for that glad day,
In my arms He'll gently lay
My precious baby. You're Jesus' little lamb.

As the last note died away, I bowed my head and once again humbly asked God to forgive me for not fully trusting in Him. He loved my baby as much as He loved me. Nothing could happen to this child without His first weighing it in His hands, the same hands that had healed the sick and raised the dead. The same hands whose tender flesh had been pierced by nails because of His great love for me. I had no idea what the future might hold, but for today I knew the peace that only God could give.

~ ~ ~

The following Saturday night my husband and I were invited to the house of some old friends. Although we lived nearby, our schedules had kept us from getting together, and it had been eight or nine months since I'd seen them and their children. The last time I had bumped into my friend and her baby, Melisa, had been at church. At that time God had given me the emotional strength to hold little Melisa without losing my composure. Now I felt a bit uncomfortable as the door opened and we were greeted by their 7-year-old son.

As we stepped inside, I marveled at how much he had grown since I had last seen him. Then I heard footsteps and looked up, expecting to see my friend. I caught my breath as Melisa, now almost 1 year old, came trotting around the corner. Suddenly she stopped, her dark-brown eyes locked onto mine, and we stared at each other for a long moment. It was almost like seeing my own child take her first steps. I watched my little namesake in delight and wonder. A part of me longed to run to her, to pick her up in my arms and never let her go. Instead, I simply waited, returning her steady gaze. *She can't remember me,* I thought. *She was just a baby. Why doesn't she turn away? She almost acts as though she understands how special she is to me, and why.*

After it seemed as though she had carried on an entire conversation with me with her eyes, she moved, stretched out her arms, and tottered toward me. I could feel her warm breath on my neck as I gently hugged her close, imagining the day when I would hold my own babies for the first time. How I would cradle them in my arms and gently kiss their tiny faces! I could almost feel their chubby fingers encircling my own. A sudden joy washed over me, a cleansing, healing joy.

My friend and her husband entered the room, and little Melisa tottered away from my grasp. Several times that night I caught her staring at me curiously, always meeting my eyes, her gaze so innocent, yet perceptive. Of course, she couldn't realize that I might have had a little girl just her age. . . .

~ ~ ~

Two days after my visit with Melisa and her parents, the bleeding vanished as silently and unexpectedly as it had come. It had stopped at the time the doctor had said it should. We were ecstatic! Nothing could contain our joy!

Ken went with me to my 12-week checkup. Finally I was through my first trimester. I knew the risk of miscarriage reduces dramatically after the first three months, since the baby is completely formed. Because of expense, a sonogram would not be done; however, we would be able to *hear* the heartbeat for the first time.

As we pulled into the parking lot, I knew something could still go wrong, but a sense of peace settled over me. God had led me this far. He would not forsake me now. Though I couldn't explain all the reasons for the trials of the past, I had learned one important lesson—*God cared about me and my baby.* Somehow the doctor's appointment no longer seemed so dreadful. I could tackle the unknown, whatever it might hold.

My mind traveled back to that heartbreaking day in October when I discovered that I was not pregnant. I remembered the anguish I felt as I wrestled with God's will for my life and the peace I received once I had surrendered all to Him. The now-familiar story of the Shunammite woman made me smile as I realized how merciful God had been in giving me such concrete evidence of the future.

Other memories flashed through my mind—the positive pregnancy test . . . waiting for the nurse's call to say the baby was developing at the correct rate—all answers to prayer. Of course, I could never forget the morning I thought I had miscarried and the seemingly endless days of spotting that followed, trying every inch of my faith.

Now, as I prepared to listen to my baby's beating heart, a new thought entered my mind: *God Himself is my every heartbeat. He is all I'll ever need. Even if I lose another baby, I will never lose Him! Both my little one and I are safe in His strong arms. He will never let us go. We are His children—His precious little lambs.*

With God by my side, I was ready to face the future.

On July 13, 1996, Melissa delivered a healthy baby boy. They named him Matthew, "a gift from God." To his grateful parents he is a living miracle and a daily reminder of the Lord's great goodness and love.

Melissa, a full-time mom, is the leader of a women's Bible study and prayer group and an associate women's ministry leader in her church. She has been trained in grief counseling and believes that God has called her to the special ministry of helping to heal hurting hearts.

Bibliography

Bordow, Joan. *The Ultimate Loss: Coping With the Death of a Child.* New York: Beaufort Books, Inc., 1982.

Canwell, Nancy. Handout from God-controlled Emotions Seminar. Unpublished paper.

Donnelly, Katherine Fair. *Recovering From the Loss of a Child.* New York: Macmillan Publishing Co., 1982.

Finley, Mark. *Studying Together.* Fallbrook, Calif.: Hart Research Center, 1991.

Hayford, Jack. *I'll Hold You in Heaven.* Ventura, Calif.: Regal Books, 1990.

Hales, Dianne R., and Johnson, Timothy R. B. *Intensive Caring: New Hope for High-risk Pregnancy.* New York: Crown Publishers, Inc., 1989.

Holford, Karen. *The Loneliest Grief.* Alma Park, Grantham, England: Autumn House Publications, 1994.

Love, Vicky. *Childless Is Not Less.* Minneapolis: Bethany House Publishers, 1984.

Rank, Maureen. *Free to Grieve: Healing and Encouragement for Those Who Have Experienced the Physical and Emotional Trauma of Miscarriage and Stillbirth.* Minneapolis: Bethany House Publishers, 1985.

Reich, Ellen Judith. *Waiting: A Diary of Loss and Hope in Pregnancy.* New York: Park Press, 1992.

Rich, Laurie A. *When Pregnancy Isn't Perfect.* New York: Dutton, 1991.

Taylor, Arlene. Whole Brain Seminar notes and handout.

Toder, Francine. *When Your Child Is Gone: Learning to Live Again.* Sacramento, Calif.: Capital Publishing Co., 1986.

Vredevelt, Pam W. *Empty Arms: Emotional Support for Those Who Have Suffered Miscarriage or Stillbirth.* Portland, Oreg.: Multnomah Press, 1984.

Appendix

HOPE AND HELP
FROM THE
SCRIPTURES

Petitioning God for a Child

Deut. 4:29	Seek the Lord, and I will find Him.
Ps. 9:9, 10	God will not forsake those who seek Him.
Ps. 37:4	God will give me the desires of my heart.
Ps. 84:11	No good thing will He withhold from those who walk uprightly.
Ps. 116:1, 2	God has heard my supplications.
Ps. 145:18-20	God fulfills the desires of those who call upon Him.
Jer. 29:11-13	God gives peace, hope, and answers prayers.
Matt. 7:7, 8	Ask, and it will be given me.
Luke 11:9-13	Ask, and I will receive. Our Father gives good gifts.
John 14:14	Ask in Christ's name, and He will do it.
John 16:24	Ask so my joy might be full.
Rom. 8:32	He will freely give me all things.
Phil. 4:19	He will supply all my needs.
Heb. 10:23	Hold fast to hope—He who promises is faithful.

| James 1:17 | Every good gift is from God. |
| 1 John 5:14, 15 | God hears all we pray. |

God Gives Peace and Comfort

2 Sam. 22:31	The ways of God are perfect, His words proven, His shield to be trusted.
Ps. 17:8	I am the apple of God's eye.
Ps. 22:9-11	God is with us from the womb.
Ps. 34:18	Near brokenhearted; saves the crushed in spirit.
Ps. 37:23, 24	The Lord will uphold us.
Ps. 40:4	Blessed is the person who makes the Lord their trust.
Ps. 42:11	Hope in God.
Ps. 55:22	Cast my burdens on Him; He will sustain me.
Ps. 91:1, 2	God is my refuge; I will trust Him.
Ps. 100:3	God made us; we are His sheep.
Ps. 147:3	God heals the brokenhearted and binds up wounds.
Prov. 3:5	Trust in the Lord. He will lead me.
Isa. 26:3	God keeps in perfect peace those whose mind is on Him.
Isa. 32:17	Righteousness, peace, quietness, assurance.
Isa. 40:11	He feeds flock, holds lambs in His arms, leads those who are with young.
Isa. 41:10	Fear not; don't be dismayed. He strengthens and holds.
Matt. 11:28-30	Come, all who are heavy laden, and receive rest.
John 10:10	Jesus gives life more abundantly.
John 14:27	Peace I leave with you.

Rom. 12:12	Rejoice in hope, be patient in tribulation, steadfast.
Rom. 15:13	The God of hope fills me with joy and peace.
Phil. 4:7	The peace of God.
Col. 2:6-10	I am complete in Christ.
1 Thess. 5:16-23	Rejoice, pray without ceasing, give thanks, hold fast what is good. The God of peace sanctifies.
1 Thess. 5:24	The God of peace is faithful; He will do it.
Heb. 13:21	God will complete His will in me.

Overcoming Trials

1 Chron. 29:14	All things come from God.
Neh. 8:10	Don't sorrow! The joy of the Lord is my strength.
Job 13:15	Though He slay me, yet will I trust Him.
Job 23:10	He knows the way and, when tested, I'll come forth as gold.
Ps. 34:19	The Lord delivers me from affliction.
Ps. 57:1-3	He's with me in calamities.
Ps. 119:71	It is good to go through trials.
Prov. 3:11, 12	Don't despise chastening—it's love.
Isa. 55:8, 9	My thoughts are not God's; my ways are not God's.
Isa. 63:9, 10	In affliction, He was afflicted. He bore and carried us.
Matt. 26:42	Jesus surrenders His will to the Father's.
Rom. 8:18	Sufferings not worthy to be compared to future glory.

Rom. 12:12	Rejoicing in hope, patient in trials, strong in prayer.
1 Cor. 10:13	God will not allow me to be tempted beyond my ability to withstand.
2 Cor. 4:17	Light affliction for a moment works for my good.
2 Cor. 7:4	Be joyful in tribulation.
Phil. 4:11, 12	Be content in all things.
2 Tim. 3:12	The godly will suffer persecution.
Heb. 4:15	Jesus sympathizes with my weakness.
Heb. 5:8	Jesus learned obedience through trials.
Heb. 12:11	Chastening seems grievous but yields peaceable fruit of righteousness.
James 1:2-5	Count it joy to go through trials. Ask for wisdom.
1 Peter 2:21	Christ, my example, suffered for me.
1 Peter 4:12, 13	Rejoice when trials come.

Don't Worry! God Is in Control

Ps. 27:14	Wait on the Lord.
Ps. 32:8	God will instruct you where to go.
Prov. 12:25	Anxiety causes depression; good words make glad.
Matt. 6:31-34	Do not worry.
Phil. 4:4-6	Don't worry: offer rejoicing, supplication, thanksgiving.
1 Peter 5:7	Cast all cares upon Him.

Birth, Children, Miscarriage

Gen. 18:14	Is anything too hard for God? He gave Sarah a son.
Gen. 30:22	God opened Rachel's womb.
1 Sam. 1	Hannah asks God for a son.
1 Sam. 2:21	Hannah receives three more sons and two daughters.

Ps. 127:3	Children are the heritage of the Lord, His reward.
Ps. 139:13-16	God has made me and formed me in the womb.
Isa. 26:16-19	Figurative miscarriage.
Isa. 44:24	God formed me from the womb.
Isa. 49:5	God formed Christ from the womb to be His Servant.
Isa. 49:15	A woman may forget the child of her womb, but God doesn't.

Chosen by God in the Womb

Judges 13:5-7	God chose Samson from the womb.
Isa. 49:1	God called Jesus by name in the womb.
Jer. 1:5	Before God formed Jeremiah in the womb, He knew him and set him apart.

Death and Grief

Ps. 126:5, 6	God will turn tears to joy.
Isa. 25:8	Death will be swallowed up forever; tears wiped away.
Isa. 35:10	Sorrow will flee away.
Isa. 60:20	Days of mourning will end.
Isa. 65:19, 20	A child a few days old will not die; no more crying.
Jer. 31:15-17	Children will be returned to parents, all sorrow gone.
John 16:20-23	Sorrow turned to joy.
Rom. 8:37-39	Nothing can separate me from God.
2 Cor. 1:3-5	God comforts those who are suffering.
1 Thess. 4:14-18	Comforting thought: those who are dead (asleep) are brought forth.
Rev. 7:17	God will wipe away every tear.
Rev. 21:4	There will be no more sorrow or crying.